HEROES
OF SERBIA

FOLK BALLADS RETOLD BY

Nada Ćurčija-Prodanović

HEROES
OF SERBIA.

FOLK BALLADS RETOLD BY

Nada Ćurčija-Prodanović

Illustrated by

DUŠAN RISTIĆ

New York
HENRY Z. WALCK, INC.
1964

PRINTED IN GREAT BRITAIN

CONTENTS

THE RISE AND DECLINE OF THE SERBIAN KINGDOM 1

Tsar Dushan's Wedding 5

King Vukashin's Wedding 19

Urosh and his Uncles 24

THE BATTLE OF KOSSOVO 29

The Building of Ravanitsa 33

Sultan Murat's Challenge 36

What Ivan Kossantchich Saw in the Turkish Camp 37

Tsar Lazar and Tsaritsa Militsa 39

Tsar Lazar's Supper 42

Milutin, Tsar Lazar's Servant 44

The Fall of Serbia 46

The Maiden of Kossovo 48

The Death of the Yugovichi's Mother 51

KRALYEVICH MARKO 55

Kralyevich Marko and the Vila 58

Kralyevich Marko and the Eagle 61

Kralyevich Marko recognizes his Father's Sabre 63

CONTENTS

Kralyevich Marko's Ploughing 67

Kralyevich Marko drinks Wine during the Ramadhan 68

Kralyevich Marko's Wedding 71

Kralyevich Marko and Alil-Aga 77

Kralyevich Marko and Mina of Kostur 80

Kralyevich Marko and the Arab 87

Kralyevich Marko Abolishes the Wedding-Tax 95

Kralyevich Marko and Mussa Kessedzhiya 100

Kralyevich Marko's Death 105

SERBIAN KNIGHTS AND OUTLAWS 109

Maksim Tsernoyevich's Wedding 111

The Sick Doytchin 126

The Brothers Yakshich divide their Heirloom 131

Old Novak and the Village Elder, Bogossav 134

Ivo Senkovich and Aga of Ribnik 136

The Kind Pasha and Mihat the Shepherd 143

Outlaw Vukossav's Wife 146

Little Radoyitsa 151

Ivan of Semberiya 155

The Beginning of the Serbian Uprising against the Turks 161

The Battle of Mishar 171

Author's note 174

Glossary 177

THE RISE AND DECLINE
OF THE SERBIAN KINGDOM

 HE Slavs came to the Balkans during the great migration, in the sixth and seventh centuries A.D. The first small states were founded in the south and southwest of the present Yugoslavia, in Macedonia, Herzogovina (then called Dukliya), Montenegro (Zeta), and in the south of what is nowadays known as Serbia (then Rashka). All of them soon embraced Christianity, which came to them mainly from Byzantium, and their religion has remained Greek Orthodox to this day. Soon after that time two Macedonian monks, Cyril and Method, devised a new alphabet which came to be called 'Cyrillic' after one of them. Somewhat altered in the course of time, it is still used in Yugoslavia, Russia, Greece, and Bulgaria.

I

Stevan Nemanya (eleventh century) was the founder of the dynasty of Nemanyichi: he was Grand Duke of Rashka—which was the name for Serbia in his day. After organizing the state and bringing order and peace among the feudal lords, he withdrew to Mount Athos in Greece, where he had built a fine monastery, Hilendar, and there he lived as a monk up to his death. After his death he was canonized and became St. Simeon. One of his sons succeeded him: he is known as Stevan the First Crowned. He was the first King of the Nemanyichi dynasty and he succeeded in winning autonomy for the Serbian Church. Sava, his youngest brother, was a monk and a very good diplomat who greatly helped his brother in state affairs. Sava was also a gifted writer who cared very much about the Enlightenment and brought it to the Serbs. His versatility and gifts became legendary: there are many stories about St. Sava (for he, too, was canonized after his death) which show him as a brave man who was always fighting against laziness, stupidity, and superstition. The influence he exerted in Serbia, both in his lifetime and after his death, was so great that the Turks, after conquering Serbia and establishing their rule there (during the fourteenth and fifteenth centuries), found it necessary to dig up his earthly remains and bring them to Belgrade. In 1594—about three hundred years after his death—they burned them on the Hill of Vratchar. Nevertheless, St. Sava continued to exert his influence and he has been considered as a patron saint of all schools and educational institutions for many, many years.

Among other kings of the Nemanyichi dynasty, Dragutin (thirteenth century) and later Milutin (thirteenth-fourteenth centuries) brought the kingdom to greatness. Milutin expanded its frontiers, brought skilled miners from Saxony to work in his silver and lead mines, and made the town of Novo Brdo (New Hill), with its forty thousand inhabitants, one of the biggest and richest in the Europe of his day. Trade with the Slavonic Republic of Dubrovnik (Raguza), with Byzantium, Venice, and other countries flourished; life in Serbia was very civilized and well organized, especially in comparison with other European countries of the same period. The capital was the town of Prizren, in south Serbia.

Dushan, first King, then Tsar (from 1346), was called 'Dushan the Mighty', for the state was at the peak of its prosperity and wealth during his reign. He made Skopliye (Macedonia) his capital and was crowned in it. He not only consolidated the frontiers of Serbia, but

2

also had drawn up and proclaimed to the people a code of laws in which he firmly regulated all aspects of public and private life in his empire. The episcopate of Pech was promoted to be a patriarchy. Tsar Dushan died relatively young and was succeeded by his inexperienced son, the boy Urosh, who ended the dynasty in 1371.

In spite of many wars which left devastation in their wake, and in spite of the many foreign armies, including Crusaders, which have marched up and down Serbia—as the valleys of the rivers Sava, Morava, and Vardar have been the most convenient roads and links between East and West for centuries—there still remain many monasteries, pious foundations of the Nemanyichi, which speak of the greatness of their founders. Their architecture and, in particular, the splendid fresco paintings adorning their walls from top to bottom speak of an original native art of great strength and beauty, bearing evidence at the same time of a high standard of living in those days; the painters often presented saints and angels in the garb of their contemporaries, seated at tables with plates, forks (which in the twelfth and thirteenth centuries were used only at King's tables in many other countries), or else working in the fields with the agricultural implements of those days. Most striking are the faces, which are bold, vivid, and so characteristic of Serbian features that one often seems to recognize them in the street, in a train, or at a village fair.

Those were the churches and monasteries Tsaritsa Militsa spoke of in the ballad about the building of Ravanitsa. And, as Milosh Obilich prophesied, the Turks did take off their roofs of lead and melt them into bullets. In some of the monasteries the Turks covered the walls of the churches with plaster and whitewashed them (which once more proves that every cloud has its silver lining, for in some cases that layer of plaster preserved the frescoes in spite of rain, snow, and hail which came through the open roofs). In other monasteries the saints' images on the frescoes were damaged by the Turks, and also by other people, out of superstition, for there was a belief that the plaster from a holy image would cure many an illness.

After the Turkish conquest the Serbs moved towards the north: there were several migration waves. One of them, the third in fact, was led by one of the Serbian Patriarchs, Tcharnoyevich. Before leaving his old country to cross the Sava and the Danube in the north and settle in Voyvodina (then under Austro-Hungarian rule), the Patriarch visited the old monastery—Sopochani—near the town of Novi Pazar

3

and, as a kind of sad leave-taking, carved his name, *Arsenië*, on the stone doorway of the roofless church. He seems to have been in a hurry, or his knife was perhaps a bad, clumsy tool, but his message could not be more poignant to posterity had the letters been carved by a master craftsman and filled with gold.

The Kings and Tsars became dust with time, but most of their pious thoughts, witnesses of their glory and power, weathered all the storms of the tumultuous and turbulent history of the Serbs.

TSAR DUSHAN'S WEDDING

WHEN Dushan the Mighty, Tsar of all the Serbs, decided to marry, he wrote a letter to the Latin King Mihailo asking for the hand of his daughter, the maiden Roksanda. Thus the Tsar proposed, and the King agreed to give him his daughter in marriage.

Having received this favourable answer, Tsar Dushan called his high dignitary, Todor the Vizier, and said to him: 'My servant, Todor the Vizier, I want you to go to the white town of Ledjane, to my future father-in-law, the King Mihailo, and make all

5

arrangements for my wedding: when we are to come with our wedding-train for the bride, and how many members my retinue should number. I also want you to see the maiden Roksanda, to judge whether she is fit to be my Tsaritsa and the mistress of this country. I want you to see her and to give her my ring in sign of betrothal.'

Todor the Vizier bowed low before his lord, and, having made his preparations, departed to the Latins.

In the white town of Ledjane, the King received him as befitted a dignitary of high rank; they feasted, drinking wine for a whole week. Then Todor the Vizier gave the Tsar's message to the King: 'My friend, King Mihailo, I have not been sent by my Tsar to drink wine in Ledjane, but to bespeak the wedding with you, to ask when my Tsar should come for his bride; and how many men he should bring with him in his wedding-train. I have also come to see the maiden Roksanda, and to place on her hand my Tsar's ring of betrothal.'

King Mihailo said to him: 'My friend, Todor the Vizier, as for the Tsar's wedding-train, he may bring as many men as he will; as for the time—he may come whenever he wishes. You will give your Tsar my greetings and with them my only request: he should not bring with him his two nephews, the two brothers Voyinovichi, Vukashin and Petrashin, for they are both very likely to pick a quarrel, and I fear they may start a brawl which would be unseemly in our peaceful, white town of Ledjane. As for the maiden, you will see her soon and give her the ring, according to custom.'

When the dark night fell, neither wax candles nor any other lights were brought in as the maiden was ushered into the chamber. All was completely dark. Seeing this, Todor the Vizier took the rings out of his purse: golden rings they were, set with pearls and precious stones. The hall glowed with the light of the jewels, and the maiden looked so beautiful to him, fairer than a white fairy; he put the Tsar's ring on Roksanda's finger and gave her a thousand ducats, his master's gift, whereupon her brothers took her away.

As dawn broke the next morning, Todor the Vizier departed and was on the road to the white town of Prizren. When he arrived at the palace, the Serbian Tsar Dushan asked him: 'Well, my servant, Todor the Vizier, have you seen my betrothed, the maiden Roksanda? Have you given her my ring? What does King Mihailo say?'

Todor told him all in good order: 'I saw her, my lord Tsar, I saw her and gave her your ring. O, what a beauty Roksanda the maiden is!

There is not her like among the Serbs! As for King Mihailo, his words were kindly: "You may go for the maiden whenever you want and take as many of your men as you wish." However, with his greetings the King sent you but one request: do not take with you your two nephews, the two Voyinovichi; they drink heavily and, when drunk, they are likely to pick a quarrel and start a brawl, which would be unseemly in the Latin city of Ledjane.'

Hearing this, Tsar Dushan struck his knee with his clenched fist: 'Woe to me! Alas, what a disgrace! So the tale of the rakish ways of my nephews, the Voyinovichi, has spread as far as that! I give you my word of honour that I shall have them both hanged on the gates of the city of Vutchitern as soon as my wedding is over, for I cannot have them disgrace me in the world!'

The Tsar set then about gathering his friends and retinue for the wedding; he collected twelve thousand men and set off with them down the vast Field of Kossovo. As they were passing under the towers of Vutchitern, the two young Voyinovichi saw them and wondered:

'What can have made our uncle so angry with us, so angry that he did not ask us to his wedding? Somebody must have told him lies about us: may his flesh rot and fall off his bones whoever he may be! There is our Tsar going to the Latin country, without a brave knight of his own kindred, without such a man who would be at his side in case of trouble. The Latins are an old, cunning race; they will behead our uncle; and yet we cannot go with him, uninvited!'

Their old mother heard them and said: 'My sons, my two Voyinovichi, you have yet another brother, Milosh the shepherd, who is now with the sheep in the mountains; he is the youngest yet the bravest among you, and the Tsar does not know him because he has never yet seen him. Send him a letter, asking him to come to Vutchitern, but do not tell him the reason; say, instead: "Our old mother is on her deathbed; she calls you to give you her blessing. Hurry down, unless you want a curse instead of her blessing to bear with you all your life long; make haste, that you may see your mother before she breathes her last." '

The brothers did their mother's bidding; they wrote the letter and sent it to their brother, Milosh the shepherd, in the mountain of Shara, saying:

'Oh, Milosh, our own dear brother, hurry down to the city of Vutchitern! Our old mother is dying and calls you to give you her

7

blessing. So come quickly unless you want to live under her curse for ever.'

When Milosh received the letter, he read it, tears streaming down his face. All his thirty shepherds asked him:

'O Milosh, our good master, letters have come before this, but you never read them with tears in your eyes! Where does this one come from, tell us, in Heaven's name?'

Milosh sprang to his feet and told his shepherds: 'O shepherds, my dear brothers, this letter comes from my home: my old mother is dying and she wishes to give me her blessing. I must go to her; guard well the sheep until I return to you.'

So Milosh went to the city of Vutchitern. As he approached he saw his two brothers, and with them his old mother coming to meet him. Milosh reproached them: 'Why, my dear brothers, did you frighten me so, and why did you make so much trouble for me, so much trouble without cause?'

His brothers answered him: 'Come along, brother, there is trouble indeed.'

The brothers embraced one another, and Milosh kissed his mother's white hand. After the greetings were over, they told him how the Tsar had gone to the far Latin country to fetch his bride, without taking his nephews with him. 'But will you, Milosh, go with our uncle's wedding-suite, uninvited though you may be? You should be there in case he meets trouble and needs you; but if that does not occur you had better return with him, without telling him who you are.'

Milosh agreed wholeheartedly. 'I will, my dear brothers! If I would not stand by my uncle, by whom else should I ever stand?'

His brothers set about preparing him for the journey: Petrashin went to harness and prepare his bay steed, and Vukashin busied himself with Milosh: he dressed him in a fine shirt, embroidered with golden thread from the neck down to the waist, all with white silk underneath; over the shirt he put three fine sleeveless jackets, and over them a splendid surcoat with thirty golden buttons and heavy gold-studded armplates; he helped him into his trousers and fixed his buckles for him; over all that he put a dark cloak such as Bulgarians usually wear. On Milosh's head he also set a black fur cap, making the youth look like a dark Bulgarian, so that his own brothers hardly knew him. They gave him the sharp pointed lance, and the beautifully wrought green sword of old Voyin, their father. Petrashin brought out his steed all wrapped up in bearskins so that the Tsar should not recognize him. Before Milosh set out, his brother gave him this wise advice:

'When you catch up with the wedding-party, they will ask you who you are and where you come from: tell them that you are from Karavlashka and that you had been serving Lord Radul who refused to pay you your due. Say then, "So I went away into the wide world, to look for a better master to serve. I heard about the Tsar's wedding and joined his train, hoping that I might be given a piece of white bread and a glass of red wine from him." Take care always to hold the reins firmly in your hands, for your steed is wont to keep abreast with the Tsar's own horses.'

Milosh mounted his steed and rode off to join the wedding-party. He reached them before long and the men in festive array asked him: 'Where do you come from, young Bulgarian lad?'

Milosh answered them as his brothers had advised him, and they welcomed him: 'Welcome to us, young Bulgarian; it is good to have one more youth with us!'

As they were advancing on the road, Milosh, who had been used to sleeping on the mountain next to his sheep about mid-day, dozed on his steed. Feeling the reins lax in his master's hands, the horse held up his head proudly and stamped through the wedding-suite, pushing to right and left the other horses and riders, many of whom fell down. So he arrived at the head of the procession. He slowed down only when he was abreast with the Tsar's own horses. The indignant lords and courtiers wanted to thrash the Bulgarian, but the Serbian Tsar Dushan held them back.

'Do not beat the young Bulgarian; the lad has been used to sleeping on the mountain by his sheep; do not strike him, but gently wake him up.'

The lords and the Tsar's courtiers shook Milosh by the shoulder saying: 'Wake up, young Bulgarian lad! Shame on your mother who bore you uncouth as you are and sent you to the Tsar's wedding!'

Startled, Milosh looked up and met the Tsar's own dark eyes; he saw where his steed was, walking abreast with the Tsar's own horses, and quickly drew the reins in and whipped his horse, who started leaping three spears in width and four in height. As for the length, it was impossible to tell how far he jumped; while out of his mouth came burning fire, and from his nostrils flared blue flames.

All the twelve thousand men stopped dead in their tracks, watching the young Bulgarian's steed and marvelling among themselves:

'Great Lord, what a wonder! What a splendid steed and what a poor rider! We have never seen his like before! There was such a horse, once upon a time, owned by the Tsar's late brother-in-law, but his sons, the Voyinovichi, own him now.'

Among those who admired the horse were three cunning men: Vuk Djakovitsa, Yanko from Nestopoliye, and a youth from Priyepoliye. Looking at the marvellous animal, they said: 'What a fine horse that young Bulgarian has! There isn't another like that in all this train. Even the Tsar's own mount is not so fine! Let us linger behind to see whether we can somehow get hold of him.'

10

As they neared a gorge the three cunning men lagged behind the others and spoke to Milosh the shepherd:

'Listen to us, young Bulgarian lad! Would you exchange that horse for another and better one? We will give you a hundred ducats to boot; also a plough and oxen to till the fields and earn your bread.'

Milosh Voyinovich replied thus to them: 'Let me be, you three cunning men! I am not looking for a better horse, for I cannot force even this one to obey me. What should I do with the hundred ducats? I could not weigh them on the scales. Why do I need the plough and the oxen? My father did no ploughing, yet he fed and brought me up well without it.'

The three shrewd men said then: 'Look now, you Bulgarian lad, if you will not agree to exchange the horse of your own free will, we shall take it by force!'

To this Milosh Voyinovich answered: 'Force can take towns and whole countries, let alone my horse! I would rather give you my horse in exchange for another, for I could not continue on foot.'

He drew rein and put his hand under the bearskin; the others thought he was taking the whip, but what he drew out was a six-knobbed golden mace. Milosh hit Vuk Djakovitsa with it. He touched him so lightly that Vuk whirled away, turning three times in the air before falling down. Milosh Voyinovich said to him then: 'May your vines in Djakovitsa bring you as many grapes as there were somersaults you made in the air!'

Yanko from Nestopoliye fled, but Milosh, riding his bay steed, caught up with him; he hit him between the shoulder-blades and Yanko turned over four times. 'Take good care of yourself, Yanko! May your trees in the gentle Nestopoliye bear you as many apples as were the turnabouts you made in the air!'

The poor youth from Priyepoliye was now running for his life, but Milosh was swift on his bay; he tapped him on the shoulder with his golden mace, and the youth rolled seven times in the air. 'Take good care of yourself, youth from Priyepoliye! When you go back home, boast to your maidens in Priyepoliye that you took the Bulgarian's steed by force!'

Only then did he join the rest of the wedding-train. When they came to the white town of Ledjane, they pitched their tents in the field. Oats were given to the horse of the Tsar and to the other horses, but there were none for Milosh's steed. Seeing this, Milosh Voyinovich hung a bag on his left arm and walked from one oat-bag to another until he had filled his own, and then he fed his horse. Afterwards, he went to the innkeeper and said to him: 'Innkeeper, give me some wine to drink!'

The innkeeper scowled: 'Go away, you black Bulgarian! Had you brought a Bulgarian wooden bowl, I might have poured you some wine in it, but these golden cups are not for the like of you!'

Milosh glanced at him from the corner of his eye and slapped him across the face: his hand was so light that three of the innkeeper's teeth fell down into his throat. The young host begged him then: 'Don't strike me again, Bulgarian! You shall have as much wine as you want, even if the Tsar must go short of it!' But Milosh did not ask him for anything now; he himself poured wine into a golden cup and drank it.

Whilst he was still feasting and drinking, daylight broke and the sun came up. A Latin youth cried from the ramparts:

'Hear me now, Serbian Tsar Dushan! There in the field beneath the city of Ledjane a knight has come out as his King's champion to fight a battle with you. You are to fight with him or you will not be allowed to depart from here, either you or any of the men in your suite; least of all will you be allowed to take away the maiden Roksanda!'

Hearing this, Tsar Dushan sent a messenger to his retinue. The messenger went about from tent to tent shouting:

'Has any mother borne and sent to the Tsar's wedding a brave knight who would be willing to fight the Tsar's battle for him? Great honours would the Tsar bestow on him.'

Alas, no such knight was to be found. The Tsar struck his knee with his fist, saying: 'Woe to me, may God have mercy on me! If I had my two nephews with me now, my two nephews, the two Voyinovichi, they would go out into the field and take up the battle for me.'

The Tsar had not yet finished speaking when Milosh came to his tent, leading his bay steed.

'My lord Tsar, may I go into the field to take up the battle for you?'

The Serbian Tsar Dushan answered him: 'You may, young Bulgarian lad, but it is not seemly! However, if you slay the King's champion, I shall reward you with great honours.'

Milosh mounted his fierce steed and turned away from the Tsar's white tent, taking his lance with the spearhead pointing behind. The Tsar said to him: 'Do not carry your lance backwards, my son! Turn the spearhead the other way round or the Latins will laugh at you.'

12

Milosh replied: 'Do not fear for me, my lord Tsar. If I find myself in danger I shall easily turn my lance the right way; if not, I can bring it back like this too.'

Saying this, he rode down the field of Ledjane. The Latin maidens who watched him from the ramparts were saying: 'Dear Lord, what a wonder! What kind of champion is that for the Tsar? Rejoice, King's knight; there is no need for you to draw your sabre out of its scabbard at all—for there is nothing to smear it with blood!'

By then, Milosh had reached the tent where the knight was sitting. His red-coated horse was tethered to a lance stuck in the ground.

Milosh Voyinovich said to him: 'Rise to your feet, young Latin knight, rise to your feet and let us fight our battle!'

But the fair-skinned Latin answered contemptuously: 'Go away, you black Bulgarian! There is nothing on which to stain my sabre! You do not even wear clothes befitting a knight of the Tsar!'

Milosh Voyinovich grew angry: 'Get up, you fair-skinned Latin lad! True, your clothes are better than mine, but I will take them off your body and wear them myself.'

The young Latin leapt to his feet, mounted his fiery steed and made a tour of the field. Milosh, meanwhile, was standing on the mark, waiting for him. The young Latin threw his lance, aiming at Milosh's breast, but Milosh thrust his golden mace forward and, receiving the lance on it, shivered it into three pieces.

The fair-skinned Latin said to him then: 'Wait a little, you black Bulgarian! I was given a faulty lance; wait till I go and take a better one,' and rode away across the field. Milosh shouted after him:

'Stop a little, you fair-skinned Latin knight! Would you run away?' And he rode in pursuit. He chased him across the field to the city gates of Ledjane, but the gates were shut. Milosh threw his lance and nailed the fair-skinned Latin lad to the door; he cut off his head, threw it into his horse's oat-bag, took the reins of the other steed and led it to his honourable Tsar.

'Here is the head of the King's young knight, my Tsar.'

The Tsar gave him riches innumerable. 'Go now, my son, and drink some wine. I shall bestow great honours upon you!' he said.

Hardly had Milosh sat down and begun to drink when the Latin herald cried from the ramparts:

'Hear, O Tsar! In the meadow beneath the city of Ledjane there are three brave chargers, armed, and with three fiery swords stuck in their

13

saddles, their flaming ends pointed skywards: you are to jump over the three brave chargers! Unless you do this you will not depart from here, let alone take your bride with you!'

The Tsar's messenger walked amongst the wedding-suite, shouting: 'Has any mother borne and sent to the Tsar's wedding a knight capable of jumping over three brave chargers with three flaming swords stuck in their saddles?'

It seemed there was no such knight to be found.

But there was the young Bulgarian who walked to the tent of the Serbian Tsar Dushan.

'My lord Tsar, may I go to the meadow and jump over the three brave chargers?'

'You may, my dear child, only I wish you would take off that dark Bulgarian cloak—may the tailor perish, the fool who cut it so badly, and so much too big for you!'

Milosh Voyinovich replied to him:

'Sit there and drink your red wine, my lord Tsar. Do not trouble yourself over my dark cloak! If there is a brave heart in a man, the cloak will not hinder him: if a sheep is troubled by its own wool, there is no good sheep or good wool either!'

Thereupon he walked down the field of Ledjane. Reaching the three brave chargers, he led his bay past them, saying to him:

'Wait for me to jump into the saddle, my brave bay horse!' He walked over to the other side, ran across the field, leapt over the three brave chargers, and over the three flaming swords stuck in their saddles, falling straight on to the back of his bay horse; he took the three brave chargers and led them to the Serbian Tsar Dushan.

Not much time had gone by before the young Latin shouted from the ramparts once more:

'Come now, Serbian Tsar, come under the highest tower in Ledjane; a spear is stuck on the top of it, a golden apple resting on its tip: you are to hit the apple through a ring with your arrow!'

Milosh did not wait for the messenger now. He went to his Tsar straight away and asked him:

'My lord Tsar, may I go and shoot my arrow through the ring at the apple?'

'Yes you may, my own dear son!'

Milosh went and stood beneath the white tower. He took aim with his arrow resting on its golden bow; he hit the apple through the ring, took it into his white hands, and carried it to the honourable Tsar, who rewarded him richly.

Soon the Latin's voice was heard from the ramparts again:

'Hear, O Tsar, the two King's sons have come out under the white fortress bringing three fair maidens with them: fair they are, all three of them. They look alike and wear exactly the same gowns; you are to go now and tell which of them is Roksanda. If you choose the wrong one, you will not depart from here alive, let alone take your bride with you!'

When the Tsar understood his words, he called Todor the Vizier: 'Go, my servant, and tell which of them is my betrothed!'

Todor swore to him: 'I have not seen her, my Tsar, for she was ushered in complete darkness into the room when I gave her your ring in sign of betrothal.'

The Tsar struck his knee with his clenched fist: 'Woe to me! May God have mercy on me! We have outwitted and conquered them so far, and now the maiden will remain here to disgrace us for ever!'

Hearing this, Milosh Voyinovich went to his Tsar.

'My lord Tsar, may I go and tell which is the maiden Roksanda?'

'Yes, you may, my dear child, but poor is my trust in you: how are you to tell which is she when you have never set eyes on her!'

Milosh replied to him: 'Do not worry, my gracious lord Tsar. When I was up on the mountain of Shara, where I kept twelve thousand sheep, it sometimes happened that as many as three hundred lambs were born in the course of one single night, and I was able to tell each lamb by its mother. I shall easily tell Roksanda by her brothers.'

The Serbian Tsar Dushan told him then: 'Go then, my dear child! If God will that you should tell which is Roksanda, I shall give the rich lands of Skenderiya into your possession for the rest of your lifetime.'

Milosh walked down the wide field. Coming to the place where the maidens were standing, he threw the Bulgarian fur cap off his head and shook the dark cloak off his shoulders. The scarlet silk and velvet glowed in the sunshine; the golden arm-plates on his breast and the buckles on his legs glistened; Milosh was blazing in the green field like the fiery sun appearing behind a mountain. He drew out of his pocket some jewels and threw them on the green grass, scattering around golden rings, pearls, and precious stones. He drew out his green sword, saying to the three maidens:

'Let the one among you who is the maiden Roksanda roll up her long sleeves and bend down to gather these golden rings, pearls, and precious stones; if any other should reach for them, I give you my word of honour that I shall cut off both her arms up to her elbows!'

When they heard this, both maidens at the ends looked at the one in the middle. She lowered her gaze to the green grass, rolled up her long silken sleeves, and gathered all the rings, pearls, and precious stones. The other two maidens ran away, but Milosh did not let them escape; he caught them both by their hands and took all three of them to Tsar Dushan. He gave him the maiden Roksanda, and another one with her to be her maid-in-waiting, keeping the third for himself.

The Tsar kissed Milosh between his eyes, without knowing yet who he was nor where he came from. The wedding heralds, all in festive array, shouted: 'Prepare and make ready, O festive wedding guests! It is time to go home!'

They were soon ready, their banners flying and pipers playing merry tunes, and all in the best order they set off; taking with them Roksanda the bride. As they drew a little farther from the town, Milosh Voyinovich said to the Tsar:

'My lord Serbian Tsar Dushan, here in the city of Ledjane there is a Duke by the name of Balatchko. I know him and he knows me. He has been in the service of the King for seven years now. The King has kept him here with only one purpose—that he should drive away the wedding-party, and take back the maiden Roksanda. The King will send him to pursue us now. Balatchko has three heads on his body: out of one of them dart blue flames, and out of the other an icy wind blows, but when these two heads are cut off, Balatchko is an easy prey. Continue your way, and take the maiden with you; I shall stay here to wait for Balatchko.'

The wedding-party rode away, taking the fair maiden, and Milosh stayed in the green forest with three hundred companions.

When the wedding-train left Ledjane, the King called Duke Balatchko:

'O Balatchko, my faithful servant, can you trust yourself to go and scatter away the Tsar's wedding-train and bring back my dear daughter, the maiden Roksanda?'

Upon which Balatchko asked him: 'My lord King of Ledjane, what kind of a knight was he who achieved the most difficult feat of arms these last few days?'

The Queen of Ledjane said to him: 'Our servant Duke Balatchko, there is not a single brave knight among them to speak of, but a young, dark Bulgarian youth; so young that his cheeks are as soft as a girl's.

16

But Duke Balatchko said then: 'No, that is no dark Bulgarian, that is Milosh Voyinovich. Although the Tsar himself does not know who he is, I have known him for a long time now!'

Thereupon the Queen of Ledjane urged him: 'Go now, our true servant Duke Balatchko, go and take my daughter from the Serbs; if you do so, I shall give her to you to be your wedded wife.'

Balatchko saddled his mare and galloped down the road after the wedding-party, accompanied by six hundred Latin soldiers. As they reached the green forest, they saw the bay standing in the midst of the wide road, and Milosh Voyinovich looking behind him. Duke Balatchko shouted to him:

'O Milosh, did you expect me?' and he breathed out a blue flame which scorched the black bearskin; seeing that no harm was done that way, he blew out an icy wind: the bay turned over three times but Milosh did not wink an eye.

Now Milosh let his voice boom loud out of his white throat:

'There is something here you have not been expecting, Balatchko!'

And he swung his golden mace at him, touching him so lightly that Balatchko was thrown out of his saddle. Milosh then threw his sharp-pointed lance and, nailing him to the green grass, he cut off all his three heads and threw them into his horse's oat-bag. He made an onslaught on the soldiers, his three hundred companions behind him. They slew three hundred men and then turned to join the wedding-party. When they reached the Tsar and his retinue, Milosh threw Balatchko's heads at his feet. The Tsar embraced him and rewarded him richly, and they all rode on to the white city of Prizren.

As they rode across the vast Field of Kossovo, Milosh, before turning off to his city of Vutchitern, thus addressed the Serbian Tsar Dushan:

'Farewell now, my dear uncle; my dear uncle, Serbian Tsar Dushan!'

Only then did the Tsar realize that the youth was Milosh Voyinovich. He said to him: 'Is that you, my child Milosh? Is that you, my own dear nephew! Happy is the mother who gave life to you, and happy is your uncle to have you for a nephew! Why did you not tell me before who you were, for, not knowing it, I let you suffer the hardships of the journey—I let you sleep on poor beds and go short of good food and red wine!'

Woe to him who is alone in the world and has no one of his own kindred!

KING VUKASHIN'S WEDDING

ING Vukashin wrote a letter from his white town of Skadar on Boyana to the town of Pirlitor in Herzegovina, on the foot-hill of Mount Durmitor; he secretly wrote it to Vidossava, Momtchilo's wife, and secretly sent it to her:

'Vidossava, Momtchilo's wife, why should you live amidst all that ice and snow? If you look up, all you can see is Mount Durmitor, crowned with ice and snow both in summer and winter alike. If you look down from your city, you can see only the wild, muddy river Tara tumbling among the rocks, carrying trunks and boulders in its wild waters; there is no bridge, nor any other way to cross the savage river, and its steep banks are all marble rocks with just a few pine-trees growing among them. Poison your husband Duke Momtchilo, poison him or betray him to me, and then come to live in my gentle coastland. Come to my white city of Skadar on Boyana; I shall take you for my faithful wife, and you will be my lady Queen. To pass the time away, you will spin silk on a golden distaff; spinning silk, you will sit on silken cushions and wear clothes of velvet and brocades, and, moreover, all my dazzling jewels. And what a place is Skadar on Boyana! Looking up at the hills above the city, you will see them covered by olive and fig trees, and also by many fine vine-terraces; looking down from the city across the steep slopes, you will see the golden wheat, and around it many green meadows. Across them flows the emerald Boyana, full of all kinds of fish which you may eat, fresh out of the river, whenever you wish!'

The letter reached Momtchilo's wife. When she had read it, she instantly answered:

'My lord, King Vukashin, it is not easy to betray, to betray or poison Duke Momtchilo: Momtchilo has a sister, Yevrossima, who cooks his choice meals for him and tastes them before him; Momtchilo has nine beloved brothers and twelve nephews: they pour out his wine and serve it to him; they drink out of each of his cups before he does. Momtchilo also has a horse, Yabutchilo, Yabutchilo the winged one who can fly wherever his master wishes, and, finally, Momtchilo has a sabre with eyes on it; he fears no one but God.

'But listen to me, King Vukashin! Raise a numerous host, bring them to the fields around the lakes and hide them in the green forest. Momtchilo has an unusual custom: every Sunday morning he goes early to hunt by the lakes, taking with him his nine beloved brothers, his twelve nephews, and his forty servants. On the eve of next Sunday I shall burn Yabutchilo's wings and I shall dip Momtchilo's sharp sabre into salty blood so that it will stick in its scabbard and he will not be able to draw it out. That is how you will be able to slay Momtchilo.'

Receiving her letter, the King was happy and he did as he was bidden: he raised a numerous host, took it to Herzegovina, reached the lakes and hid with his men in the green forest.

In Momtchilo's mansion, on the eve of that Sunday, Momtchilo went to his bed-chamber and lay down on soft mattresses. Soon after him his wife came in too, but she would not lie on the bed: she stood above him with tears running down her face. Momtchilo asked her: 'Vidossava, my faithful wife, what is tormenting you and making you shed these tears above my head?'

Young Vidossava said to him: 'My dear lord Duke Momtchilo, nothing is tormenting me, but I have heard a very strange thing. I have heard it, but not seen it so far: they say that you have a horse, Yabutchilo, Yabutchilo the winged one. I have never seen those wings of Yabutchilo and am afraid that you might lose your life through him.'

Wise he was, Duke Momtchilo, wise he was, yet he made a mistake and thus spoke to his wife: 'Vidossava, my faithful wife, I can easily put your mind at rest. All you need do, if you wish to see the horse's wings, is to go to the new stables at cock-crow, for it is then that he spreads out his wings and you will be able to see them.' Saying this, he closed his eyes and went to sleep.

Momtchilo was sleeping, but not his wife. Lying on the bed at his side, she was listening to hear the first cocks crow. When she heard them, she jumped from the bed, lit a candle, and went straight to the new stables. What Momtchilo had said was true: Yabutchilo had spread out his wings and unfolded them so that they reached to his hoofs. Vidossava now spread grease and tar all over the wings and set fire to them with her candle, so that Yabutchilo's wings were burned; all that did not burn out she tacked together and tied firmly under his belly. She then went to the armoury, took Momtchilo's sabre, and dipped it in salty blood. Only then did she return to the soft mattresses on their bed.

When at dawn the sky grew light, Duke Momtchilo rose and said to his wife Vidossava: 'Vidossava, my faithful wife, I had a strange dream last night: I saw in my dream a wisp of fog rising from the accursed lands of Vassoye; I saw it come over and encircle Mount Durmitor; I struck through that fog with my nine beloved brothers, my twelve nephews, and my forty soldiers, but we all lost each other in the fog. Thus we parted, never to come together again; I fear, wife, that this portends no good.'

Vidossava said to him: 'Fear nothing, my dear lord! A brave knight may dream whatever dream comes to him, yet dreams are false and only God is true!'

Duke Momtchilo prepared for the hunt then and went down from his white tower; his nine beloved brothers, his twelve nephews and forty soldiers were all in the courtyard, awaiting him. His wife led his horse to him and waited upon him as he mounted into the saddle. All his company leapt on horseback after him and rode away to the hunt by the lakes.

As the hunters approached the lakes, they were surrounded by the host which had been lying in wait for them. Seeing them, Momtchilo reached for his sabre, but it was held fast as if it had grown into its scabbard. Duke Momtchilo said then: 'Listen to me, my dear brothers! The cunning Vidossava has betrayed me: give me the best of your sabres.'

The brothers immediately complied with his wish and gave him the best of their sabres. Momtchilo then said to them: 'Listen to me, my beloved brothers! You go and attack the flanks of the enemy's host, and I shall strike my way through their midst.'

What a wonderful sight it was! If only you could have seen Momtchilo striking with his sabre right and left, and clearing the road to the mountain for himself! His horse Yabutchilo was even fiercer than he, stamping down more enemies than his master was able to slay with his sabre. But bad luck met Momtchilo as he emerged from the enemy host, riding toward the town of Pirlitor: nine black horses came up to him, nine horses, but not a single one of his brothers in their saddles!

As Momtchilo saw that, his brave heart broke in his breast with grief for his own brothers. His white arms grew weak and he could strike not a blow more; he spurred his horse Yabutchilo, spurred him on and kicked him with his riding-boots, urging him to leave the ground and fly over to the city of Pirlitor, but the horse could not spread his wings and take off from the ground. Duke Momtchilo cursed him: 'Yabutchilo, may the wolves devour you! How many times have we flown from here, without any real need, just for pleasure! Remember, my horse! And now you will not do it to save my life!'

His horse answered him, neighing: 'O my master, Duke Momtchilo, do not curse me, or try to force me, for today I cannot fly; may God strike your wife Vidossava dead! It was she who burnt my wings, and the little that was left of them after the fire died down she tucked under my belly and tied firmly with the reins. So run away on foot for your life, dear master!'

Hearing that, Duke Momtchilo shed tears and jumped from his saddle; in three leaps he was at the city gates, but the gates were closed, closed and bolted! Seeing his plight, Momtchilo called his sister Yevrossima:

'Yevrossima, my own dear sister, let down a white linen sheet, that I may climb up to the city and escape the foe!'

The sister answered her brother, weeping: 'Oh, my brother, Duke Momtchilo, how can I let down the white linen sheet when my sister-in-law, my sister-in-law, your treacherous wife, has tied my hair to the rafters?'

His sister had a soft, loving heart; she was very sorry for her brother, and crying out like a snake caught in a cleft, she shook her head and tore off her hair which remained tied to the rafters; she then snatched a white linen sheet and let one end down over the city ramparts. Momtchilo caught it and began to climb up the walls; he had almost reached the ramparts when his treacherous wife ran to him, holding a sabre, and cut off the linen above his hands. Momtchilo fell down the walls, landing on the upturned swords and spears, on the cudgels and maces of the King's soldiers. They threw him from one to another until he reached King Vukashin, who hit his heart with his battling-lance. Momtchilo said to him with his last breath:

'Hear my dying words, King Vukashin: do not marry my Vidossava, Vidossava my treacherous wife, because she will be your undoing too: today she has betrayed me to you and tomorrow she will betray you to another man. Take for your wife my dear sister, my dear sister Yevrossima, for she will always be faithful to you and will bear you a son, a brave man as I have been.'

Whilst saying this, Duke Momtchilo was struggling with his soul, and as soon as he finished speaking, he breathed his last.

When Duke Momtchilo died, the city gates were opened and out walked the treacherous Vidossava to welcome King Vukashin; she took him to the white tower, set him at the golden table and brought to him wine, brandy, and all sorts of dainty food. Afterwards she went to the armoury and brought out Momtchilo's clothes, Momtchilo's own clothes and arms. But you should behold the wonder then: that which had reached Momtchilo's knees dragged on the floor when Vukashin wore it; that which Momtchilo had worn as a helmet fell down on to Vukashin's shoulders; that which had been one of Momtchilo's boots was big enough for both of Vukashin's legs; that which Momtchilo had worn as a golden ring, Vukashin had to wear over three fingers; that which Momtchilo had used as a sabre dragged a yard on the ground behind Vukashin; and that which had been a light blanket to Momtchilo weighed so heavily on the King that he could not rise from beneath it!

King Vukashin said then: 'Woe to me! Alas, may God hear my repentant voice now! Look at that cunning Vidossava! When she betrayed such a brave knight, a brave man without his like in the world today, how can I trust her not to betray me tomorrow!'

He summoned his servants and they caught Vidossava, tied her to the horses' tails, drove the horses down Mount Pirlitor and she was torn asunder.

The King ransacked Momtchilo's mansion, and took with him Momtchilo's sister, Yevrossima, down to Skadar on Boyana and married her, taking her for his wedded wife. He had two fine sons by her, Marko and Andriya. Marko took after his uncle, his uncle, the brave Duke Momtchilo.

UROSH AND HIS UNCLES

OUR parties met on the Field of Kossovo, by the white church of Samodrezha: the first was King Vukashin's party, the second was that of Despot Uglyesha; the third belonged to Duke Goyko, and the fourth was that of the young Tsarevich, Urosh. Each of them coveted the vacant throne of the Serbian Tsar, and was prepared to fight for it and to stab his rivals with his golden knife; each of them believed that only he should inherit the Empire.

King Vukashin said: 'The throne is mine!'

Despot Uglyesha said: 'No, it is mine!'

So said Duke Goyko too: 'No, it is mine!'

24

The boy Tsarevich Urosh kept silent, not daring to say a word, for fear of his three uncles, his three uncles, the three Murniyavtchevichi.

King Vukashin wrote a letter and sent it by his messenger to the white town of Prizren, to the priest Nedelko, asking him to come to the Field of Kossovo and say to whom the Empire should go: for the priest had given the illustrious Tsar the last unction and heard his confession; moreover, he possessed old books which would help him to find out the truth.

Despot Uglyesha also wrote a letter, and sent it by his messenger to Prizren to the same priest, for exactly the same reason. Duke Goyko and the young Tsarevich Urosh did the same. All four of them sent their messengers secretly, not wishing the others to know what they had done.

However, the four messengers met in the white town of Prizren, at the home of the priest Nedelko. As it was Sunday, the priest was not at home, but in church, serving the early liturgy.

The haughty, short-tempered messengers, more arrogant even than their masters, rode to the church and, without dismounting, entered the holy place of worship and started to whip the priest Nedelko with their plaited whips:

'Hurry now, priest Nedelko, hurry and come with us to the vast Field of Kossovo and say to whom the Empire should go. You gave the last unction to the late illustrious Tsar, you gave him the unction and heard his confession; moreover, you possess the old books of wisdom. If you do not obey us, you will be beheaded!'

The priest Nedelko wept and said to them:

'Go away, arrogant messengers! Leave me to finish the holy liturgy; after that you will know to whom the Empire should go.'

When the service was over, they all left the church, and the priest Nedelko spoke thus: 'My children, four mighty messengers, indeed I gave the illustrious Tsar his last communion and I heard his confession; but I asked him then not about the crown, but about the sins he had committed in his lifetime. Therefore you had better go to the city of Prilep, to the palace of Kralyevich Marko who was once my pupil; I taught him to read and write, and afterwards he became clerk to the Tsar. The old books of wisdom are with him and he will certainly know to whom the Empire should go. Ask Marko to go to Kossovo with you; he will tell you the truth, for Marko fears no one but God the Almighty.'

The four messengers departed, and rode to the city of Prilep, to the white palace of Kralyevich Marko. Arriving there, they struck the door with the heavy iron knocker. Marko's mother, Yevrossima, heard their knocking and called her son:

'My son Marko, my dear child, who is it knocking so hard at the door? It sounds as if it might be your father's messengers coming here.'

Marko rose and opened the door.

'God be with you, my lord Marko!' the four messengers greeted him, as one.

Marko answered: 'Welcome, my dear children! How are the Serbian knights; how are the honourable Kings and Tsars?'

The messengers bowed humbly to him: 'Our good lord, Kralyevich Marko, they are all in good health, but there is no peace between them: our lords are quarrelling bitterly on the vast Field of Kossovo, by the white church of Samodrezha. They all covet the crown, and are prepared to stab each other with their golden knives and to murder each other for it, because they do not know to whom the Empire should go. They all ask you to come to the Field of Kossovo to tell them who is to inherit the Empire.'

Marko walked back into his princely palace and called to his mother Yevrossima:

'Yevrossima, my dear mother, our mighty lords have quarrelled bitterly over the crown on the Field of Kossovo, and they ask me to go to them now, to tell them who is to inherit the Empire.'

Although Marko himself was a very righteous man, still his mother, Yevrossima, begged him:

'Marko my son, my only dear child, if you do not want me to curse you, take care: let not your judgement be swayed by any feelings you may have for your father or for your uncles. Be not unjust, but observe the righteousness of our only true Lord! Let not your soul be lost by a wrong judgement! Losing your life is better than losing your soul!'

Marko took his old books of wisdom and prepared himself for the journey. He threw himself on to his piebald horse, Sharats, and rode off to the Field of Kossovo.

As the two of them neared the King's tent, King Vukashin said: 'Happy am I: may my thanks rise to Heaven! Here comes my son Marko; he will say the Empire is mine, for he will inherit it from his father.'

Marko heard him, but said nothing; he passed the King's tent without even glancing at it. Seeing him, Despot Uglyesha cried: 'Happy am I: may my thanks rise to Heaven! Here comes my nephew! He will say the Empire is mine. Speak, Marko, and we shall rule together, like two loving brothers!'

Marko kept silent, and, without uttering a single word, he passed the tent, without even glancing at it.

Duke Goyko caught sight of him then and cried: 'Happy am I: here comes my nephew! He will say the Empire is mine! When Marko was a small boy, I cherished him dearly and carried him always, pressing him to my breast as if he were a golden apple; wherever I rode in those days, I always put Marko on my horse and took him with me. Say, Marko, the Empire is mine, and you will be the first to rule over it; I shall sit at your knee and help you!'

But Marko kept silent, and rode on without once glancing at the tent of his uncle. He rode straight to the white tent of the boy Tsarevich Urosh, and at the doorway of the tent he dismounted. When the boy Urosh saw him before the tent, he leapt up from his silken cushions, he leapt to his feet and said: 'Happy am I: here comes my godfather! He will say to whom the Empire should go.'

They opened their arms wide, embraced and kissed each other, and inquired about each other's health. Then they sat down on the silken cushions and the boy Tsarevich Urosh offered his guest refreshment after his journey. Before long the day was gone and the dark night began. But the next morning, as soon as it grew light, the church bells pealed out and all the lords went to early liturgy. When the prayers were over they walked out of the white church and sat at the tables spread in the churchyard, eating sweets, roasted meats, and drinking plum-brandy.

Marko took his old books of wisdom and spoke before them all, looking at each in turn: 'O my Father, King Vukashin, is your Kingdom not enough for you? Does it not suffice you—may it become a waste desert!—but you have to fight for somebody else's lands?

'And you, my uncle, Despot Uglyesha, is your Despotdom not enough for you? Does it not suffice you—may it become a waste desert! —but you have to fight for somebody else's possessions?

'You, too, my uncle, Duke Goyko, is your Duchy not enough for you? Does it not suffice you—may it become a waste desert!—but you have to fight for somebody else's Empire?

'Do you not see—may God never see any of you!—that the books say: the Empire belongs to Urosh! He inherited it from his father; he is his rightful heir and it is to him that the Tsar left the Crown in his dying hour, before going to eternal rest.'

Hearing this, King Vukashin leapt to his feet, and drew out his golden scimitar to stab his own son Marko. Marko fled from the King because it would not be seemly for him to fight with his own father; he ran round the white church of Samodrezha, with his father the King in pursuit. When they were rounding the church for the third time his father almost caught up with him, but suddenly a voice was heard from within the church:

'Run into the church, Kralyevich Marko! Don't you see that you are going to fall today, to be killed by your own father for having told God's truth!'

The church door opened itself to Marko, and he ran inside; the door closed behind him. The King hurled himself at the church door and struck one of the posts with his golden scimitar. As he did so, blood dripped from the wood.

The King repented, wailing: 'Woe is me! May God have mercy on me—I have slain my own son, Marko!'

But a voice spoke from within the church: 'Hear me, O King Vukashin! It is not Marko you have slain, but one of God's own angels.'

The anger returned to the King who bitterly cursed his son now: 'My son Marko, may God kill you! May you never be blessed with your heart's offspring! And may you live to serve the Turkish Sultan!'

While the King was thus cursing Marko, the young Tsar was blessing him: 'Godfather Marko, may God always help you! May your face always shine with honour among your equals! May your sabre always be victorious in battle! May there never again be a hero like you, and may your name be remembered as long as the sun and the moon shine from the skies!'

Both these prophecies were to come true later on, but Marko, hearing them then, did not know.

28

THE BATTLE OF KOSSOVO

A DEFEAT WHICH BECAME A VICTORY

*'IF all of us were to turn into salt, there would not be enough of it to season
a dinner for the Turkish host.'*

 ERY, very numerous and mighty, Sultan Murat's
Turkish hosts were pushing up from the south of the
Balkan Peninsula. After passing through the Byzan-
tine Empire and winning the battle on the river
Maritsa in Bulgaria, they threatened the Serbian
lands.

It was not only a question of a foreign force threatening Serbian independence: it was to be the contest between an Islamic, Moslem power and Christianity.

Although the Serbian Tsar Lazar and his dignitaries, Serbian lords and knights, knew that there was hardly any chance of winning the battle, they stood their ground bravely and fought to the last man on 28 June 1389. Vuk Brankovich, according to the legend, kept his men away from the battle and his name therefore became a synonym for 'traitor'. Historically, however, he was not guilty of treason.

The day of the battle came to be called 'Vidovdan' by posterity, which means, as Tsar Lazar said: 'the day when it will be seen who is true and who untrue', also 'the day when it will be seen to whom the Empire will belong'. However, as Tsar Lazar had been offered the choice between the spiritual and the secular kingdom, and had, as the legend has it, chosen to embrace the kingdom of Heaven, there could be little doubt as to the outcome of the battle. According to the same ballad, all the Serbian lords and their hosts were prepared to die on the battlefield and were administered the holy communion. And yet there was hope in all their hearts, hope against reason, almost against certainty—bright human hope for survival, as shown in the ballad about the maiden of Kossovo. Vidovdan has always been celebrated as a national holiday, in memory of all the brave Serbs who fell on the Field of Kossovo.

And the Field itself seemed unable to forget the battle, either, for every spring, in May and at the beginning of June, the whole vast field is covered by peonies, red with the blood of the Kossovo heroes, as legend has it.

Two monuments stand, clearly outlined against the blue sky, on the wide, gently undulating field: the place has been marked where Tsar Lazar fell, never to be forgotten, and, not very far from it, there is the Turkish tomb of Sultan Murat who was slain by Milosh Obilich.

Dead long ago, all those heroes and brave knights—Tsar Lazar, Old Yug Bogdan (Tsaritsa Militsa's father) and his nine sons, the nine Yugovichi, Milosh Obilich, Ivan Kossantchich, Pavle Orlovich, and others—still live in the hearts of all Serbs. Their readiness to fight and die for a lost cause (which even they realized was hopeless) gave courage to many Serbs in later days when times were often harsh, and they inspired them to follow their example and, eventually, to win the battle for their own lands and freedom.

30

This group of Kossovo ballads is unique in that it is the only full, complete cycle telling of an historical event and sung by anonymous folk poets some time after the event. It has come down to posterity in all its tragic greatness and beauty. The origin of these ballads may, perhaps, be ascribed to the need of an enslaved people for some bright, unsullied memory which would be glorious enough to make life in their plight bearable; to the pathetic need for a solace which would, like a blazing torch, light the way into the future and link it with the splendid past, passing over the gloomy darkness of their own day.

THE BUILDING OF RAVANITSA

HE illustrious Tsar Lazar was celebrating his patron saint's day by a feast, to which all the Serbian lords were invited. The Tsar set them at the long table, giving each of them the place he was entitled to by his rank and age. At the head of the table the Tsar himself sat and they all began drinking the cool wine, engaging in pleasant conversation. When the feasting was at its highest, in came Lady Militsa, Tsar Lazar's wife, richly dressed, her precious jewels glistening in the festive light of the hall: nine rows of pearls adorned her white neck; a golden crown with three great diamonds, dazzling by day and night alike, was on her head. Lady Militsa walked along the hall and, passing before Tsar Lazar, said:

'My lord, illustrious Tsar Lazar, although it is not seemly that I should look at you, let alone speak to you in such noble company, I have to say what preys on my mind. The old dynasty of Nemanyichi ruled our lands and, when their time was over, they went to their graves. But they did not accumulate heaps of gold and treasures in their vaults and caskets; instead they built many churches and monasteries to ensure rest for their souls. Thus they built Vissoki Detchani above the town of Djakovitsa; they built the patriarchy of Pech in the hills above Pech, St. Peter's Church near Novi Pazar, and not far from it the splendid Sopochane by the cool river of Rashka. They also built the majestic Studenitsa amid the wooded mountains, the graceful Gratchanitsa on the Field of Kossovo, and many other monuments,

33

nestling on the mountain-sides or by the cool swift rivers of Serbia. All these are their pious foundations. You inherited their throne and amassed heaps of treasure without building one single church to ensure rest for your soul; all those riches can be of no good for our souls or for our bodies either. Neither we nor any of ours will have any benefit from them.'

Tsar Lazar said then: 'Do you hear what Lady Militsa says, Serbian lords? I will build a church by the river of Ravan and call it Ravanista; I have as much wealth as I could wish for. I shall have the foundations of my church made of lead, the walls of white silver, the roof of glistening gold, and I shall adorn it all over with pearls and precious stones.'

All the lords rose to their feet and bowed to him: 'Do so, our lord Tsar; it will earn peace for your soul and good health for your son, the noble Stevan.'

But Milosh Obilich, who was sitting at the opposite end of the table, did not get up or say a word. Tsar Lazar noticed this and spoke, toasting him with a golden cup:

'May you enjoy good health, Duke Milosh! I wish you would say something about my intention to build this church.'

Milosh lightly jumped to his feet, took off his fur-lined helmet and went over to pay homage to the Tsar: he was given a golden cup. Raising it in his hand, he cried:

'Thank you for your noble speech, my liege lord! But as for your intention of building the church, I must say that this is no time for it, and it cannot be; take the wise old books, my lord Tsar, take them and see what they have to tell us: our days are numbered, and the Turks are going to take our lands over: before long the Turks will rule here; they will pull down our famous churches, our noble monasteries and your church Ravanista along with all the others. They will dig out its lead foundations and melt them into cannon-balls which they will use to destroy our cities and towns; they will pull down the silver church-walls and make armplates and harnesses for their chargers; they will take off the golden roof and make collars and chains for their heathen wives; the pearls from your church will adorn their necks, and the precious stones will be set in the hilts of their sabres, their *yataghans*.

'But hear me now, illustrious Tsar Lazar! Let us dig out marble from the mountain-sides and let us build a church of stone: even though the Turks may take over our lands, our churches will live on and serve for worshipping God until the Judgement Day: from stone nobody can take anything but stone.'

Hearing him, Tsar Lazar answered Duke Milosh: 'Thank you, Duke Milosh! Thank you for your noble speech, for all you said was pure honest truth.'

And so his church was built of stone, and weathered through all the storms and battles.

SULTAN MURAT'S CHALLENGE

ULTAN Murat reached with his mighty host the Field of Kossovo and wrote a letter to Tsar Lazar who resided in his city of Krushevats.

'O Tsar Lazar, head of Serbia! It has never been, nor can it ever be, that one land be ruled by two lords; that one people pay taxes to two masters. We cannot rule over Serbia, both of us. Send me therefore the keys and the taxes—the golden keys of all your towns and the taxes for seven past years.

'If you do not do my bidding, come to the Field of Kossovo. Let our sabres decide to whom the country shall belong!'

Receiving the letter, Tsar Lazar was greatly disturbed and worried.

He decided to accept the challenge and, along with the summons to all his lords and subjects, he let a curse fall on those who should dare to disobey his call for battle:

> 'Let him who fails to join the battle of Kossovo
> Fail in all he undertakes in his fields.
> Let his fields go barren of the good golden wheat,
> Let his vineyards remain without vines or grapes!'

WHAT IVAN KOSSANTCHICH SAW
IN THE TURKISH CAMP

F all of us were to turn into salt, there would not be enough of it to season a dinner for the Turkish host.

I have seen all over the immensely vast field; all of it is covered by the Turkish host: horse pressed to horse, lances close one to another, looking like a dense black forest; their flags flapping in the wind like clouds, their white tents close to one another—like white snow on the mountains.

'If rain were suddenly to pour down, not a single drop would fall on parched soil, but on good chargers and their brave riders,' said Ivan Kossantchich to his friends, the Serbian knights, after reconnaissance among the Turkish hosts.

'Where is the tent of the Turkish Sultan Murat, tell me, Ivan my dear sworn brother?

'I pledged my word to my lord, the Serbian Tsar Lazar, that I would slay the Sultan on the Field of Kossovo,' Milosh Obilich said eagerly.

'How foolish you are, my dear brother! Sultan Murat's tent is in the very midst of the Turkish host.

'Even if you had a falcon's strong swift wings and were to fall by his tent out of the blue, you would not be able to fly back with your feathers and flesh unharmed,' replied Ivan Kossantchich.

'O Ivan, my dear brother, do not tell our lord, Tsar Lazar, what you have now told us: he would be assailed by worry for his men, and our soldiers would hear of it and become frightened.

'You had better tell Tsar Lazar that the Turkish host is numerous, true, but say that most of the soldiers are either inexperienced youths who have never seen a battle, or old men and muezzins who hope to profit by the war between our two sides. Moreover, tell him that both their soldiers and horses have been victims of various illnesses and are no serious challenge to us.

'Say we can fight with them and win the day, dear brother.'

TSAR LAZAR AND TSARITSA MILITSA

s Tsar Lazar sat down for supper one evening, Tsaritsa Militsa joined him, and sitting at his side, she said:

'Tsar Lazar, golden crown of Serbia, you will go to the Field of Kossovo tomorrow, taking with you all your dukes, courtiers, and servants. Not one of them will you leave at home: there will be nobody to take my letter to you to Kossovo and bring back your answer to me, if need be. You are also taking with you my nine dear brothers, the nine Yugovichi. Leave me at least one of them, I beseech you, so that I, their sister, shall have a brother to cherish and swear by.'

'Which of your brothers would you most wish to have with you in our white palace?' asked Tsar Lazar, wishing to please her.

'Leave Boshko Yugovich with me, please.'

'My lady, Tsaritsa Militsa, when daylight comes next morning and the sun appears above this world, when the city gates open tomorrow, walk and stand by the gate through which all our host, our horsemen with their battling lances, will pass on their way to Kossovo. At the head of them all will be your brother Boshko Yugovich, carrying a flag with the sign of the holy Cross on it. Give him my blessing, lady Tsaritsa, and tell him that he may stay at our palace with you; as for the flag, let him give it over to him among his companions whom he deems worthy of it.'

Tsaritsa Militsa was pleased by his answer. She hardly slept that night, fearing that she might be late to catch her brother before he went to Kossovo. She rose very early next morning and was standing by the city gate when Tsar Lazar's host approached on the way to the battlefield.

At the head of the numerous host was Boshko Yugovich, riding a chestnut horse whose hair shone in the sun like copper; Boshko's helmet and gold-studded armplates glistened brightly; his sister's eyes were almost dazzled by his look of splendour, but the big flag, of costly silk with the holy Cross embroidered upon it in gold, flapped in the morning breeze and occasionally covered the rider's armour. The flagpole had a shining golden apple at its top, and the flag had at the edges a golden fringe which gently tapped Boshko between the shoulder-blades as he advanced on his horse.

Tsaritsa Militsa stepped forward, held his horse by the bridle, and embraced her brother as he bowed to her to see what she wanted. She whispered into his ear:

'O dear brother, Boshko Yugovich, the Tsar has given you to me; he has given you his blessing and has agreed for you to stay away from the battle of Kossovo and to abide with me at the town of Krushevats. Give the flag to one of your companions and return to our palace with me, beloved brother.'

Boshko shook his head and answered: 'Go back to your white tower, dear sister. I would not turn back nor give the flag with the holy Cross out of my hands even if the Tsar should make me a present of his fine city of Krushevats. Nothing would induce me to do it and give cause to my friends to say: "Look at the coward, Boshko Yugovich! He did not dare to go to Kossovo, to shed his blood for the holy Cross, and die for his Christian faith!" '

He raised his head proudly and rode through the city gate in such beauty and splendour that he almost wounded his sister's heart.

Old Yug Bogdan, his father, arrived after him, followed by seven of his sons. Tsaritsa Militsa stopped each one of them, begging them to stay with her, but they all refused to comply with her wish, gently yet firmly.

Her brother Voyin was the last to come by; he was mounted on a fine grey charger, leading the Tsar's battle horses, their harnesses and trappings bright with golden adornments.

Tsaritsa Militsa seized his horse's reins desperately, embraced her brother and said, beseeching him: 'Oh my brother, Voyin Yugovich, stay away from the battle; come back to Krushevats with me. The

Tsar gave you his blessing and advised you to give over the horses in your charge to whomsoever you should choose to replace you. Come back with me, brother, I implore you!'

'Go back to your white tower, dear sister, for I would not return with you, or give the Tsar's battle horses to anyone, even if I knew that I were to die! I am going to the Field of Kossovo, dear sister, to shed my blood for the holy Cross and to die with my brothers for our Christian faith.'

He spurred his grey horse and passed through the city gate following the others, whilst his sister, Militsa, fainted and fell down on the pavement. She was still lying on the cold flagstones, unconscious, when Tsar Lazar happened to pass by on his way to Kossovo. He saw his wife and, his heart full of sadness and tenderness for her, he turned round calling his servant:

'My good servant, young Goluban, dismount your white horse now, take up your mistress in your arms and carry her to the white tower. Stay with her, my faithful Goluban; I give you leave to absent yourself from the battle on the Field of Kossovo.'

The servant heard his words, tears streaming down his face. He did his Tsar's bidding and carried his mistress to the white tower, but could not resist the call of battle: as soon as he had left her lying on silken cushions Goluban hastened back, mounted his snow-white horse, and galloped after all the other Serbs to the vast Field of Kossovo.

TSAR LAZAR'S SUPPER

HE Serbian Tsar Lazar was celebrating his patron saint's day in his town of Krushevats. All the Serbian lords were invited to the festive supper and Tsar Lazar set them all at the table. At his right was old Yug Bogdan and next to him his nine sons, the nine Yugovichi. At the Tsar's left was Vuk Brankovich, and at the other end of the table, opposite the Tsar, sat Duke Milosh Obilich with two other Dukes, Ivan Kossantchich and Milan Toplitsa, at his sides.

Looking at all of them, Tsar Lazar took a golden beaker full of wine and spoke to his guests:

'Whose health shall I drink? If I am to drink the toast according to age, I should drink it for old Yug Bogdan; if I am to toast the most distinguished among you, I should drink it for Vuk Brankovich; if by affection, then I shall toast my nine dear brothers-in-law, the nine Yugovichi; if by beauty, I shall toast Ivan Kossantchich; and if by height, then Milan Toplitsa. If I am to toast the bravest knight among you, I shall drink this for Duke Milosh. To nobody else shall I drink this, but to Milosh Obilich! May God give you good health, Milosh, both faithful and unfaithful one! First faithful, then unfaithful will you prove to me! You will betray me tomorrow on Kossovo and go over to the Turkish Sultan Murat! May you enjoy good health, and now drink this toast; drink the wine and take the golden beaker!'

Milosh leapt up to his nimble feet and bowed low, almost touching the ground:

'Thank you, illustrious Tsar Lazar! Thank you for your toast, for the toast and your gift, but not for your speech! For—may God prove me true—I never have been unfaithful and never shall be. Tomorrow, on the Field of Kossovo, I intend to give my life for Christianity! The unfaithful one sits next to you and sips his cool wine—it is the accursed Vuk Brankovich. Tomorrow is the fine holy day of Vidovdan and we shall see who is true and who untrue! I swear by God Almighty that I shall go to Kossovo, and slay the Turkish Sultan Murat. If God and good luck grant it that I should return to Krushevats unharmed, I shall catch Vuk Brankovich, tie him to the warrior's lance, as a woman ties wool to her distaff, and thus I shall carry him to the Field of Kossovo!'

MILUTIN,
TSAR LAZAR'S SERVANT

T wo black ravens, flying from the vast Field of Kossovo, alighted on Tsar Lazar's white tower. One of them crowed as the other said:

'Is this the illustrious Tsar Lazar's tower? Is there nobody in it?'

Only Tsaritsa Militsa heard their voices and walked up to them. 'Tell me in God's name, you two black ravens, where did you come from? Are you coming from the Field of Kossovo? Have you seen two mighty hosts? Have the two hosts fought their battle? Which of them has carried the day?' she asked eagerly.

'Indeed we do come from the Field of Kossovo, Tsaritsa Militsa; we saw the two mighty hosts which fought their battle yesterday. Both Tsars fell in the battle; as for the others, there are some on the Turkish side who survived, but those few who did on the Serbian side are all wounded and bleeding, our lady Tsaritsa Militsa.'

Hardly had they finished speaking when the servant Milutin came, riding a horse all smeared with blood. He carried his right arm in his left, and, moreover, had seventeen wounds on his body.

'What is it, servant Milutin? Have you betrayed your Tsar on the Field of Kossovo?' Tsaritsa Militsa said, seeing him.

'Take me down off this brave charger, my lady Tsaritsa; take me down and wash my face with cool water. Wash me with cool spring water and give me red wine to drink, for heavy are my wounds, my lady Tsaritsa,' said the servant wearily.

Tsaritsa Militsa hastened to help him dismount, washed him with cool water and gave him red wine to drink. Seeing that he had recovered a little, Tsaritsa Militsa asked him anxiously:

'What happened on the Field of Kossovo, Milutin?
'Where did our illustrious Tsar Lazar fall?
'Where did my father, old Yug Bogdan fall?
'Where did my brothers, the nine Yugovichi fall?
'Where did Duke Milosh fall?
'Where did Banovich Strahinya fall?'

'They all fell and remained on Kossovo for ever, my lady Tsaritsa. Where Tsar Lazar fell, many lances have been broken, battling-lances, Turkish and Serbian, yet more of the Serbian lances were broken defending their lord, their lord and ours, the glorious Tsar Lazar. Old Yug Bogdan, your father, Tsaritsa, fell in the first clash of the two hosts. Your brothers, the eight Yugovichi, fell fighting and avenging each other. Boshko Yugovich outlived them, my lady Tsaritsa; when I left the field, wounded and bleeding, he was still chasing Turkish posses across the field, his silken flag with the holy Cross waving behind him; fierce and proud, he resembled a falcon in pursuit of pigeons.

'Where the blood was knee-high, that is where Banovich Strahinya fell. As for Milosh, my lady Tsaritsa, he fell by Sitnitsa, the clear river of ice-cold water; many Turks fell there too. Milosh slew the Turkish Sultan Murat and, beside him, twelve thousand Turks. May she who gave life to him be for ever blessèd in heaven. He left a memory to the Serbian people, a story to be remembered, a name to be mentioned and cherished as long as there are men in this world, as long as there is Kossovo.

'As for Vuk Brankovich, my lady Tsaritsa, may he himself and she who gave life to him be accursed for ever! May his seed and his kin be accursed, for he betrayed our Tsar on the Field of Kossovo and took away twelve thousand men, all on horseback with armplates and good arms, my lady Tsaritsa!'

THE FALL OF SERBIA

GREY falcon spread his wings and flew away from Jerusalem, carrying a swallow on his back. That was not a grey falcon, but it was Saint Iliya; and that on his back was not a swallow, but a letter from the Virgin which he was carrying to the Serbian Tsar on Kossovo. He dropped it on the Tsar's knees, and the letter began speaking by itself:

'Honourable Tsar Lazar, what Kingdom will you embrace now? Is it to be the Kingdom of Heaven or the Kingdom of this world? If you choose the earthly one, saddle your horses, tighten the reins! Let all your knights take up their sabres and rush all together among the Turks—all the Turkish hosts will perish by your hands. But if you prefer the Kingdom of Heaven, then build a church on the Field of Kossovo, not with marble but with pure silk and brocades, and let your host take holy communion in it, for they shall all die, and you with them, my Tsar.'

Hearing those words, the Tsar thought to himself:

'O Almighty Lord, what am I to do now? How shall I make up my mind which Kingdom to choose? Shall I embrace the Kingdom of

Heaven, or the earthly one? If I decide to embrace the secular Kingdom, it will not last long, being transitory as all on this earth is, whilst the heavenly one will last through all eternity.'

So the Tsar made up his mind and chose the Kingdom of Heaven. He built the church in Kossovo, as the bird had told him, all of silk and brocades, and not of marble, and invited the Serbian Patriarch as well as his twelve bishops to come and administer the last communion to his hosts.

Hardly had the last soldiers received it when the Turks made an onslaught on the Field of Kossovo. The old Yug Bogdan collected his army, and with his nine sons, the nine Yugovichi, each of them commanding nine thousand men, and with his own twelve thousand besides, he rushed at the Turks. They all fought fiercely and slew seven Pashas; when they were attacking the eighth old Yug Bogdan was slain, and after him fell his nine Yugovichi, his nine sons like nine grey falcons, and with them all their host.

The three lords Murniyavtchevichi rushed into the battlefield now: Despot Uglyesha, Duke Goyko, and King Vukashin, each of them followed by thirty thousand brave soldiers. They fought the Turks bitterly and slew eight Pashas; by the ninth Pasha, two brothers Murniyavtchevichi, Despot Uglyesha and Duke Goyko were killed, and the third one, King Vukashin, was badly wounded. The Turkish cavalry ran over him and their horses finally killed him, trampling upon him. The whole army of these three Serbian lords fell to the last man.

Now the Archduke Stepan made an onslaught, backed by his sixty thousand men. They fought the Turks like angry lions and slew nine Pashas, but as they reached the tenth, the Archduke Stepan was slain, and with him all his sixty thousand soldiers.

The Tsar of all the Serbs, Lazar, rushed among the Turks with his seventy-seven thousand men, chasing the Turks across the vast Field of Kossovo. They were so fiery and brave that it seemed as if they might carry the day. And so it would have been but for Vuk Brankovich who betrayed Tsar Lazar, his own father-in-law. Thus the Tsar perished and with him all his soldiers, the seventy-seven thousand Serbs.

And all that was holy and honourable and agreeable to God the Almighty.

THE MAIDEN OF KOSSOVO

HE maiden of Kossovo rose early of a Sunday; she went out long before sunrise, rolled up her long white sleeves above her elbows, put a bag full of white bread on her shoulders, and took two golden beakers into her hands, one full of cool water and the other of red wine. She went down to the vast Field of Kossovo and walked over the battlefield, looking at the fallen knights and soldiers, turning them over to see whether any of them were still alive. Those who showed signs of life she washed with cool water, gave them the red wine as the holy communion, and fed them with white bread.

Going thus from one warrior to another she came to Pavle Orlovich, the Tsar's young standard-bearer. He, too, was alive but very badly wounded. The maiden dragged him from the pool of blood where he was lying, washed his face and wounds, and gave him wine and bread. After a while, the young knight's blood began to pulse more vigorously in his veins and he spoke to the maiden:

48

'My dear sister, maiden of Kossovo, what sad and great misfortune makes you walk across this field and turn over warriors lying in blood? Whom do you seek on this battlefield, young maiden? Is it a brother, a nephew, or perhaps your old father?'

The maiden of Kossovo answered Pavle:

'My dear brother, unknown warrior, I am not seeking any one of my kindred, either brother, or nephew, or my old father. But perhaps you will be able to tell me what I want to know. When Tsar Lazar had the twelve bishops and thirty monks administering holy communion to his soldiers for three whole weeks, three famous Serbian dukes arrived at the church of Samodrezha. One of them was Duke Milosh, the other Ivan Kossantchich, and the third Milan Toplitsa. I happened to be in the doorway then and saw Duke Milosh approaching the church: what a wondrous sight he was then! His long sabre was clattering on the pavement, and on his head he wore a silk-lined helmet adorned with beautiful plumes. He had a silk scarf round his neck, and a fine cloak on his shoulders; he looked around and, seeing me, took his fine cloak off his shoulders and handed it to me:

' "Take this cloak, young maiden; by this cloak and by my name remember me, maiden: I shall die in the battle, fighting for our honourable Tsar. Pray for me, my dear soul, pray that I may return unharmed, and if good luck should be with you too, I shall take you as a bride for Milan, Milan my beloved sworn brother, and I shall marry the two of you and be your witness at the wedding, your wedding *koom*!"

'After him came Ivan Kossantchich: he too was a fine sight to behold. His long, shining sabre hung by his side; a dazzling, plumed helmet adorned his head, and he too had a silken scarf round his neck and a fine cloak on his shoulders. On his finger glistened a large golden ring. He looked round, saw me, and came to me handing me his golden ring with these words:

' "Take this golden ring, fair maiden; by this ring and by my name remember me, maiden. I, too, am prepared to die on the battlefield, fighting for our honourable Tsar. Pray for me, my dear soul, and if God and good luck wills it that I should return unharmed, I shall take you as a bride for Milan, my sworn brother, and I shall be his best man, his *stari svat* at the wedding."

'At last came Milan Toplitsa, arrayed as splendidly as his two sworn brothers; on his arm he carried a fine veil woven of pure golden thread. Seeing me, he took the golden veil off his arm and gave it to me.

' "Take this golden veil, fair maiden," he said; "by this veil and by my name remember me, maiden. I also shall die fighting for our honourable Tsar. Pray for me, my dear soul, for if I come back unharmed, I shall take you for my dear wife."

'Thereupon the three dukes went away. It is them I am seeking on this battlefield, unknown warrior.'

Pavle Orlovich shook his head, saying:

'Can you see, my dear sister, maiden of Kossovo, can you see where those battling-lances are highest and most numerous? Blood was as high as the horse's reins and the rider's waist there: that is where all the three of them fell!

'Go home now, go home, lest you soil your skirts and your sleeves with blood, fair maiden.'

As she heard his words, tears streamed down the maiden's face and she walked home wailing as loud as her voice would carry:

'Woe to me, unfortunate that I am! If I was to touch a green pine-tree now, even that would dry up at the touch of my accursed hand!'

THE DEATH OF THE
YUGOVICHI'S MOTHER

GOD Almighty, what a wondrous sight that was when the Serbian hosts pressed heavily down upon the Field of Kossovo! The nine young Yugovichi fought there and their father, the old Yug Bogdan, was the tenth Yugovich on the field.

Their mother prayed ardently, imploring God to give her the sharp eyes of a falcon and the mighty wings of a white swan to carry her above the vast Field of Kossovo so that she might see

her nine sons, the nine Yugovichi, and the tenth one, the old Yug Bogdan.

God heard her prayer and granted her the sharp eyes of a falcon and the mighty wings of a white swan, and she flew then as far as Kossovo.

She found them all dead, her nine dear sons, the nine Yugovichi, and the tenth one, the old Yug Bogdan. At their heads, nine battling-lances were stuck in the ground; nine falcons were perched on their lances; nine good chargers were tethered to the lances, and nine angry lions stood by the horses.

When they saw her, the nine horses neighed, the nine angry lions roared, the nine falcons screeched; but the mother made hard her heart and shed not a single tear.

She then loosed the nine horses and the nine angry lions, and collected the nine proud, grey falcons, and returned to her sad white mansion.

Daughters-in-law had been waiting for her and they saw her coming from afar off; they opened the gates and went forth to meet her. When they met, the daughters-in-law saw by her looks what had happened, and the nine widows wept bitterly for their lost husbands; their nine children cried for their fathers; the nine horses neighed for their riders, the nine angry lions roared, and the nine proud grey falcons screeched for their masters. But the mother made hard her heart even then and shed no tear for her nine sons, the nine Yugovichi and the tenth one, the old Yug Bogdan.

At about midnight, however, Damyan's piebald whinnied in his stable. Calling her daughter-in-law, Damyan's wife, the mother asked:

'Daughter-in-law, and Damyan's beloved, could you tell me, why does Damyan's piebald scream so? Is he hungry for the good and white wheat? Is he thirsty for the Zvetchan water?'

'Mother-in-law, Damyan's own mother, he is not hungry for the good and white wheat, nor is he thirsty for the Zvetchan water, but he has been wont to munch his oats until midnight and then to carry his master off for a ride. He is mourning his dead master now.'

The mother made hard her heart then, too, and shed no tear at those words.

Early next morning two black ravens flew over their white mansion. Strange they were, the ill-fated birds: their wings were blood-bespattered up to their shoulders; their beaks and breasts covered by white foam. They carried a warrior's arm, with a golden ring glistening on the hand; and this they dropped in the mother's lap. The mother of the nine Yugovichi took the arm, and, turning it over in her lap, called her daughter-in-law.

'Daughter-in-law and Damyan's beloved, could you tell me whose arm this might be?'

'Mother-in-law, Damyan's own mother, this is the arm of our dear Damyan; I know it only too well, mother, for I know this golden ring. That is Damyan's wedding ring, dear mother.'

The mother took the hand again, and turned it over and over in her lap, speaking softly:

'My hand, my dear green apple, where did you grow, and where were you plucked off?

'You grew on my own lap, beloved hand, and you were torn off on the Field of Kossovo!'

The mother could stand it no longer. Her heart broke with grief for her nine sons, nine sons, the nine Yugovichi and the tenth one, the old Yug Bogdan.

KRALYEVICH MARKO

 UR-LINED helmet low over his scowling brow, his bushy black moustache spreading wide above his mouth, jet-black eyes which looked daggers at whoever dared to cross him—and he was easily crossed, his temper being at its worst when he was roused from sleep—his fur-lined surcoat turned inside out when he was angry, Marko was a terrifying sight indeed. Endowed with extraordinary physical strength, he had an extraordinary appetite too: very fond of good red wine he was, but he seldom drank it out of a cup. Basins had to be brought out, golden or silver ones if possible, and Marko would enjoy himself by drinking the red wine and giving half of it to his inseparable companion, his brave steed, the huge piebald Sharats, or Sharin, as he was often called. There must have been a perfect communion between the two of them, and great love too, for neither of them failed to notice the slightest change in the other's mood, to inquire for the cause of it, and to try to put matters right again. The

six-knobbed golden mace hanging on the side of the saddle—the mace whose light touch put many a villain to eternal rest—these complete the portrait of Kralyevich Marko, King Vukashin's son.

'King' in Serbian is 'Kral', and 'Kralyevich' means 'Prince Heir to the Crown', which Marko was.

Alas, he never inherited his father's crown, for the Turkish victory over the Serbs on the Field of Kossovo put an end to Serbian Kings, Tsars, and their heirs for five whole centuries.

Although terrifying to look at, Marko was loved and admired by all Serbs, for he was a true knight: he put his prowess and all his earthly possessions in the service of the poor and wronged. He would always seek revenge for wrongs inflicted either upon him personally, or upon anyone else—it was all the same to him.

He was an upright man with a kind heart which made him ready to help not only people but also animals and birds, as illustrated by the ballad about the eagle and his young ones.

Among people to whom he did good turns in this way or that was, according to the legend, the Turkish Princess, daughter of Sultan Bayazeth. Her father had to acknowledge Marko's noble service, although Marko was a Serb, the vanquished enemy and now his vassal, and he came to call him 'my foster-son'. Marko in his turn called him 'foster-father'. Many, however, were the occasions when the Sultan was only too eager to see the back of his beloved foster-son, who had a strange habit of coming into his presence armed, and sitting close to the mighty Sultan. If their conversation took a ticklish turn—which it most often did, for Marko was summoned only when complaints about his behaviour annoyed the Sultan beyond endurance or when an otherwise invincible enemy had to be dealt with—Marko was wont to move closer and closer, his mace or sabre across his knees, until the Sultan was cornered and had nowhere to move to escape him. Which, in fact, made the result of the conversation quite unexpected—for the Sultan, at least.

Besides being strong, proud, and righteous, Marko was also known as a man with a great sense of humour—as he showed when he brought his mother the fruits of his first ploughing.

A legendary figure, whose likeness to the man of that name actually living in those days remains vague and hard to ascertain through the mists of unruly times, Kralyevich Marko looms high above the many other knights and heroes, as though the anonymous poets wanted him to embody all the salient traits of the Serbian character—several times larger than life of course. Also, his prowess, his quarrelsome temper and his many victories in individual contests, as sung of in these ballads, may be the expression of a conquered people to justify and explain his position as a Turkish vassal which, no doubt, must have hurt and worried them.

KRALYEVICH MARKO AND
THE VILA

WO sworn brothers were riding over the beautiful mountain of Mirotch. One of them was Kralyevich Marko, and the other was Duke Milosh. Their horses were abreast, and their lances in line: pleased with the day, they talked gaily as they rode. After a while, however, feeling sleepy on his horse Sharats, Marko turned to his companion, saying:

'O my brother, Duke Milosh, I can hardly keep my eyes open; sing a song for me to keep me awake!'

Duke Milosh answered him: 'O my brother, Kralyevich Marko, I would sing to you, but dare not because of Vila Raviyoyla; last night I drank too much wine with her in the mountain and she threatened that she would send her arrows into my throat and pierce my heart if she ever should hear me singing again.'

Kralyevich Marko urged him nevertheless: 'Do sing, brother, and do not fear the Vila as long as I, Kralyevich Marko, my far-seeing horse, Sharats, and my golden six-knobbed mace are at your side!'

Milosh yielded to his brother's entreaty and started to sing. A beautiful song it was, one of the best and oldest songs, about the Kings of Macedonia, about churches they built for the peace of their souls. Marko enjoyed the song so much that he leaned aside on his saddle and dozed as he listened. So Marko was sleeping and Milosh was singing as they rode on.

Vila Raviyoyla heard him in the mountain and sang back; Milosh was singing and the Vila answered singing in her turn, but Milosh's voice was stronger and clearer than Vila's. This angered her so much that she leapt up in the midst of Mount Mirotch, took her bow and two white arrows, and shot them at Milosh: one of them hit the Duke in his throat and the other pierced his brave heart.

Milosh cried out: 'Woe is me! Woe is me, Marko, my sworn brother! Woe, my brother: Vila has struck me with her white arrows! Did I not tell you that I ought not to sing in Mount Mirotch?'

Marko, startled from sleep, saw with horror what had befallen his sworn brother Milosh. He tightened the reins on his piebald horse Sharats, coaxing and kissing his noble steed:

'O, Sharo, my own right wing! Carry me now to Vila Raviyoyla, catch her as she flees, and I shall make you horseshoes of pure silver, of pure silver and glistening gold; I shall make you knee-long silken trappings with fine fringes reaching to the ground; I shall plait golden threads into your mane and shall adorn it with precious pearls. But if you do not reach the Vila, I shall pluck out both your eyes, break your legs, and leave you here in the woods to end your days crawling from one fir tree to the other, miserable and restless as I shall be without my sworn brother Milosh.'

He lay low on Sharats's shoulders and sped up Mount Mirotch. Vila was flying over the peaks and Sharats sailed like a whirlwind over the mountain, but without ever catching sight of her. When at last he caught a glimpse of Vila, Sharats leapt three spears in height and four spears in length and caught up with her. Seeing what danger she was in, Vila flew up in the sky, just under the clouds, but Marko swung his mace and hit her mercilessly between her shoulder-blades. He very soon brought her down on to the black earth. As she lay there, he continued to beat her with his golden six-knobbed mace.

'Why, Vila—may God kill you now!—why did you murder my sworn brother? Go and find herbs to restore him to life, or you will not carry your head on your shoulders much longer.'

Vila started to plead: 'Be by God and Saint John my sworn brother, Kralyevich Marko, and let me go to the woods of Mirotch to pluck the herbs which will heal the young Duke's deadly wounds.'

Marko, honouring God and being gentle at heart, let Vila go into the woods. She went about, plucking herbs on the Mount of Mirotch and calling sweetly to Marko every now and then: 'Here I am, my sworn brother; I shall soon return to you!'

She plucked all the herbs which she needed and took them to Duke

E

Milosh. She rubbed them in and healed the young Duke's wounds so well that Milosh's sweet singing throat sang even better than before, and his brave heart was even stronger.

The Vila then departed to Mount Mirotch, and Marko rode on with his sworn brother to the country of Poretch; afterwards they crossed the river Timok, near a village, and rode off to the country round Vidin, in Bulgaria.

The Vila, however, stayed on the mountain and said to her friends: 'Listen to me, all you other Vilas! Let not your arrows fly at any young knight as long as Kralyevich Marko lives, as long as he has his far-seeing Sharats and his golden, six-knobbed mace! For hear what I have suffered from him! I barely escaped with my life, O my dear sisters!'

KRALYEVICH MARKO AND THE EAGLE

ARKO was lying by the roadside, his body covered by his green cloak and his face by a thin, gold-embroidered handkerchief; by his head he had stuck his lance into the ground, and Sharats, his horse, was tethered to it. On the top of the lance an eagle was perching, his wings spread so wide as to make shade for the wounded warrior. From time to time he would fly down to the stream and bring back cool water in his beak to refresh the knight. Seeing this, a Vila spoke from the mountain:

'I beseech you in the name of God, tell me, grey eagle, what did Kralyevich Marko do for you that you should try so hard to make shade for him and to give him cool water to drink?'

The grey eagle answered her:

'Be silent, Vila! How can you ask what Kralyevich Marko did for me? But hear me, if you wish to know and be wiser for it: when the two hosts clashed on the Field of Kossovo, where so many were slain, and when both Tsars, the Serbian Tsar Lazar and the Turkish Sultan Murat, lost their lives in the battle, blood rose so high on the Field that horses and soldiers floated upon it as if on a stream flooding over the fields. We birds, hungry and thirsty, flew hither and thither to feed and drink our fill. My wings dipped in the blood and the fiery sun from the clear skies shone on them and my feathers soon grew sticky and rigid. I could not flap my wings to fly away and, as my companions had gone, I was left alone on the Field, trodden over by maddened horses and fierce warriors.

61

'God sent Kralyevich Marko to me then; he picked me up out of the brave men's blood, put me on Sharats, on the saddle behind him, carried me to the green mountain and left me on the branch of a fir-tree. Rain came down from the sky and washed my wings clean. Soon afterwards I was able to spread my wings again and fly away to join my companions.

'The second good deed Marko did me was this—take heed of it and be wise, Vila: when the town in the Field of Kossovo was burnt to ashes, and in the town a tower, on whose ruins my young ones were, Marko came and saved them. He put them inside his shirt and carried them to his white mansion, feeding them and caring for them for a whole month and then a week more. As they grew strong, he let them go and they returned to me in the mountain.

'That is what Marko did for me, Vila!'

And that is how Kralyevich Marko's name is remembered: by his good deeds—the same as a happy day in a troubled year.

KRALYEVICH MARKO RECOGNIZES
HIS FATHER'S SABRE

 TURKISH maiden rose at the crack of dawn one morning and went down to the river Maritsa to bleach her linen. The water was clear till the sun came out, but afterwards it grew suddenly dark, and red with blood; flowing by, the water bore with it horses and warriors' helmets. Before noon-time, wounded warriors were floating down the river too. One of them drew near to the Turkish maiden and started to turn in the whirlpool.

Seeing her, he shouted:

'Be by God my sworn sister, fair maiden, and throw me a sheet of linen! Save me out of the river Maritsa and I shall reward you richly for your good deed!'

The kind-hearted maiden threw the end of a sheet to him, dragged him to the river-bank and helped him to climb out of the water. The warrior had seventeen wounds on his body, which was covered by strange clothes the like of which the maiden had seen never before; he had also a fine sabre with a triple golden hilt adorned with three precious stones. The splendid sabre was worth three whole towns of the Tsar.

The wounded warrior spoke to the Turkish maiden: 'Sworn sister, O fair Turkish maiden, who lives with you at your white mansion?'

'My old mother and my brother, Mustaf-Aga,' answered the maiden.

'Turkish maiden, oh my sworn sister, go and bid your brother Mustaf-Aga to carry me over to your white mansion. I have with me three purses, each with three hundred golden ducats; I shall give you one of those purses, the other I shall give to your brother Mustaf-Aga, and the third I shall keep for myself, to have my wounds healed. If God wills it and if I recover, I shall reward again both you and your brother.'

The maiden left him and, returning home, said to her brother:

'O my brother, beloved Mustaf-Aga, I dragged a wounded warrior out of the river Maritsa; he has three purses full of golden ducats—one for you, one for me, and one for himself to have his heavy wounds healed. Do not make the mistake of slaying him, dear brother; go and bring him here to our white mansion.'

The Turkish youth went to the river, and found the wounded warrior and his precious sabre. Dazzled by it, he brandished it wildly and cut off the warrior's head. He then took the splendid clothes off his body and returned to his white mansion.

His sister walked to meet the two men, but seeing her brother return without the wounded warrior, she wailed: 'Why, in God's name, O why did you slay my sworn brother? What made you commit such a sad mistake, such a dreadful sin? It was his fine sabre, no doubt, O brother! May it cut off your head, too, one day!'

Saying this, she ran away and up the tall tower.

After some time, Mustaf-Aga was summoned by the Turkish Sultan to join his army. He hung the splendid sabre at his side and rode away, obeying his lord's orders. As soon as he joined the army, he caused a great stir by his unusual weapon: everybody admired it and many tried to draw it out of its scabbard, but without success. Going from hand to hand, the sabre came to Kralyevich Marko's and—lo! What a wonder!— the sabre came straight out of its scabbard!

Marko looked at the sabre and saw on it three Christian letters: one of them was the initial of the smith, Novak, who had wrought it, the second was that of his father, King Vukashin, and the third was his own, Kralyevich Marko's.

Turning to the Turk, Mustaf-Aga, Marko asked: 'Tell me, by God, Turkish youth, how did you find this sharp sabre? Did you buy it with gold? Did you win it in battle? Did your father leave it to you, or did your wife perhaps bring it to you as her dowry?'

'What you ask me, I shall truly answer, Marko,' said the Turk Mustaf-Aga, and, indeed, he told him all that had happened not long ago, on that day by the river Maritsa.

'Why, Turkish youth, why, in the name of God, why did you not attend to his wounds; why did you not help him to recover? Had you done so, I would have made the

Sultan give you lands and riches of all kinds,' said Kralyevich Marko.

The Turk smirked: 'Don't brag and be foolish, you Serb, Marko! If you could bestow lands and riches, it is for yourself that you would have won them first. Stop that idle talk and give me back my fine sabre!'

But Marko just brandished the sabre in the air and—off came Mustaf-Aga's head. The other Turks ran to the Sultan to tell him what Marko had done. The Sultan sent a servant to summon him into his imperial presence. Marko heard the order, but behaved as if he had not—he remained sitting just where he was, frowning and drinking the dark-red wine. One servant after another called him in vain, till at last, annoyed at being disturbed, Marko put on his fur-lined jacket, turning it inside out, as he did whenever he was angry, and repaired to the Sultan, carrying his heavy mace in his right hand. He walked into the Sultan's tent, sat down on the costly rug still wearing his boots—a thing nobody else would dream of in the Sultan's presence—and looked at the Sultan from the corner of his bloodshot eyes.

Seeing him in that mood, with his mace so nearby, the Sultan moved a little farther away on the cushions, but Marko drew nearer to him. The Sultan moved away once again, but Marko kept moving too until, finally, the Sultan was sitting by the wall and could move no farther. He put his hand into his silken pockets and drew out a hundred ducats which he handed to Kralyevich Marko, a wry smile on his face:

'There, Marko, my son, go and drink some wine; who made you so angry and why, I wonder?'

'Do not ask me, O Tsar, my foster-father! I recognized my dear father's sabre; I only wish it had been in your own hands, for I would have been as angry as I now am and would have done the same thing again.'

Saying this, Marko rose, frowning darkly, and walked out of the Sultan's tent without once glancing back.

KRALYEVICH MARKO'S PLOUGHING

NE day Kralyevich Marko was sitting with his old mother, Yevrossima. They were drinking wine and talking together. After a while his mother told him: 'O my son, Kralyevich Marko, give up your fighting—it is evil, and from evil no good can ever come; besides, your old mother is weary with washing your bloodstained clothes. Take instead a plough and a pair of oxen and go to work the fields in the vales and on the mountain slopes. Sow the white wheat to feed me and yourself.'

Marko obeyed his mother: he took a plough and a pair of oxen, and went to plough the Sultan's high roads—instead of the fields in vales and on the mountain slopes. Suddenly the Turks appeared on the road, carrying three loads of treasure; they said to Kralyevich Marko:

'Listen, Marko, do not plough the high roads!'

'Listen, you Turks, do not walk over my ploughing!'

'Listen, Marko, do not plough the high roads!'

'Listen, you Turks, do not walk over my ploughing!'

Very soon Marko lost patience: he heaved his plough and oxen and with them killed the Turks. He took their three loads of treasure and gave them to his old mother, saying:

'This is what I ploughed for you today, mother!'

KRALYEVICH MARKO DRINKS
WINE DURING THE RAMADHAN

ERALDS proclaimed Sultan Suleyman's order throughout his Empire, announcing that during the Moslem fast, the Ramadhan, nobody should drink wine, wear fine green surcoats, carry sabres hung on their belts, or dance the *kolo* with their wives.

But—Marko danced the *kolo* with the women folk, Marko carried his sabre, hung on his belt, Marko wore a fine green surcoat and Marko drank wine during the Ramadhan. Moreover, he urged the Turkish muezzins and effendis to drink wine with him. The Turks, offended, could not stand this and they went to their Sultan:

'Sultan Suleyman, who are both father and mother to us,' they said, bowing low to him, 'have you not forbidden us to drink wine during the fast of Ramadhan, to wear fine green surcoats, to carry sabres on our belts, and to dance the *kolo* with our wives? Yet Marko does all this, and, what is worse, he urges our muezzins and effendis to drink wine with him!'

The Sultan summoned two of his messengers at once. 'Go now, my two young messengers, go and tell Kralyevich Marko that the Sultan asks him to come and talk with him.'

The messengers departed in all haste. They found Marko sitting beneath a tent with a huge cup of wine before him, and gave him the Sultan's message. Marko was very angry at being disturbed; he struck the messengers with his cup, one after the other, and they were both lying unconscious on the ground when Marko walked out and rode away to see the Sultan.

He walked straight into the Sultan's presence and sat on the cushions at his right. Marko's fur-lined helmet was low on his brow; he put down his mace beside him and laid his sharp sabre across his knees.

'My foster-son, Marko,' said the Sultan Suleyman, 'have I not issued an order by which nobody may drink wine during the Ramadhan, wear a green surcoat, carry a sabre, or dance the *kolo* with his wife? Some good men came to me and told me evil stories about you, saying that you have disobeyed my order, and, moreover, that you were urging our muezzins and effendis to drink wine with you! Why are you pulling your fur-lined helmet down lower on to your brow? Why are you drawing your mace nearer? And why are you handling the sabre on your knees, Marko?'

'Sultan Suleyman, O my foster-father, if I drink wine during the Ramadhan, my Christian faith allows me to do so. If I force the Moslem muezzins and effendis to drink with me, I do it because my honour would not let me enjoy a good drink whilst others just sit by and watch me—let them not come to the inn where I drink wine, Sultan, my foster-father, if they are not going to join me.

'If I wear a fine green surcoat—I am a young warrior and it is seemly that I should do so!

'If I carry a sharp sabre hung on my belt, it is mine—I bought it dearly and may well do so.

'If I dance the *kolo* with the women, I may well dance it, being still a bachelor—you know well how one feels then, for you, too, my Sultan, must have been a bachelor once!

'If I pull my helmet lower over my eyes, it is because my brow is burning—talking to a Sultan is no joke, believe me.

'If I draw my mace closer to me, and handle the sabre on my knees, it is because I fear a quarrel might flare up any moment now, and if that should happen, let him next to me beware!'

The Sultan glanced around quickly and saw that no one was nearer to Marko than he was himself. He quickly moved away, but Marko drew closer to him again. The Sultan moved still farther, and Marko pressed nearer until he cornered the Sultan against the wall so that he could move no farther.

Glancing once more at the fearful, scowling warrior, the Sultan drew a hundred golden ducats out of his pockets and handed them to Kralyevich Marko, doing his best to appear at his ease.

'There, Marko, take this and go; drink some more wine,' he said, heaving a sigh of relief and mopping his brow as Marko walked out of his presence.

KRALYEVICH MARKO'S WEDDING

NE evening, as Marko sat down to supper with his mother, she spoke to him:

'O my son, Kralyevich Marko, your mother is getting old, very old indeed: she cannot prepare your supper for you as she used, she cannot serve you your red wine, nor can she hold the torch to light this hall for you any longer. Marry a wife, my dearest son, so that I may give over my duties to her whilst I am still alive and able to teach her your ways.'

'I have been through nine kingdoms, my dear old mother,' answered Marko, 'and I went into the tenth, the Turkish Empire, too; but where I found a maiden to my liking, I did not find her family suitable for you, and where her family would have been to your liking, the maiden was not to mine. There was just one who would have suited us both, my dear old mother: I saw her by the water near the palace of the Bulgarian King Shishman. As I looked at her the earth seemed to turn around me! That is the bride for me and a good family for you. Prepare bread-cakes for me and I shall be off to ask for the maiden's hand.'

The old mother was so pleased by his words that she could not wait for the morning; she baked the cakes that very night, and when Marko rose the next morning they were all ready for him to take on his journey. This he did, after preparing himself and his horse Sharats; he hung a skin full of wine on one side of his saddle and his heavy mace on the other. Now he threw himself on Sharin's back and rode away

71

straight to the country of Bulgaria, to the white palace of her lord, Shishman. The King saw Marko from afar and rode out to welcome him. They embraced warmly and kissed as old friends do, each of them inquiring after the other's health.

Faithful servants took their horses and led them to the stables; the King led Marko up into his white tower and sat with him at the table. They ate, and drank the good red wine. After some time, when they had drunk to their hearts' content, Marko leapt up quickly, took off his cap, and bowed very low, asking the King to give him his daughter in marriage. The King was delighted and agreed at once to let her marry Marko, who, according to custom, now gave the maiden his ring and an apple, in sign of betrothal. By the time he had had the costly clothes for his bride prepared, and had purchased splendid gifts for his sisters-in-law and their mother, he had spent three whole loads of treasure.

The wedding was to be in a month's time, both parties agreed, for Marko would need as much time as that to collect his wedding-party and come back for the bride. Before he left the King's palace, the maiden's mother, the Queen, spoke to him:

'My son-in-law, Marko of Prilep, do not bring as your witness at the wedding, your *koom*, somebody who is no kin to you; bring your brother or one of your nephews, for our daughter is much too beautiful. We fear that her beauty might tempt your *koom* to be unfair to you and try to commit some shameful deed.'

Marko spent that night in the palace, and early next morning he rode on his Sharats' back to the white town of Prilep. His mother, who had been waiting impatiently for him, spotted him from her high tower and walked out to meet him. When Marko came near, she opened her arms wide, embraced him, and kissed his forehead, whilst Marko kissed his mother's white hand.

'O my son, Kralyevich Marko, have you travelled unmolested? Have you proposed, and have you been promised a faithful bride who will be also a dear daughter to me?' the mother asked as they walked together to the palace.

'Yes, dear mother, I have had a good, peaceful journey and have betrothed the maiden to be my bride before long. I spent three loads of treasure on gifts to the bride's family. But that is not what worries me, mother; I am greatly worried by something else: that is by the Queen's warning. She said I ought to bring as my *koom* either a brother or nephew, for the beauty of my betrothed is such that it might easily tempt any other man and lead him to betray me. Alas, Mother, I have no dear brother, either brother or dear young nephew to take with me to the wedding now.'

His old mother stroked his hand and said to him: 'My dear son, Marko of Prilep, do not let that trouble you. Write a letter to the Duke of Venice: ask him to be your *koom* at the wedding and to bring five hundred men for the festivity. Send another letter to your friend Styepan Zemlyich; ask him to be your *stari svat*, your best man, at the wedding, and to bring another five hundred men. If you do that there is nothing for you to fear, as both of them are worthy, honest men, I trust, and true friends, my son.'

Marko obeyed his mother and wrote letters to the Duke of Venice and to his sworn brother Styepan Zemlyich, inviting them to his town of Prilep. Before long they both came, each leading five hundred men. When the wedding company was thus assembled, they rode all together to the Bulgarian King Shishman. The King received them joyfully and led them to his white castle where the noble guests feasted with their host for three whole days and nights. On the fourth morning, however, heralds cried, calling the wedding guests to make preparations for their journey home. 'The days are short and the nights long, and we all want to return to our homes,' they said.

The King came out of his palace and presented the wedding gifts, as the custom required: some men of the party received fine handkerchiefs, some others shirts; all the gifts were embroidered with golden thread. The Duke of Venice, as the *koom*, was given a large dish of pure gold, and the *stari svat* a splendid, gold-embroidered shirt; the King gave him also a good steed, mounted by the young bride, and said: 'Here is the young maiden and the horse; take my daughter safely to Marko's white mansion and this brave battle horse is yours, dear friend.'

The wedding-suite started on its way home, riding across the great Bulgarian plain. But, where there is good luck, misfortune is not very far away: a wind started blowing all of a sudden and lifted the veil which was hiding the young bride's face. The Duke of Venice, who was at her side, saw her and at once fell passionately in love with her. He could hardly wait for their night's rest; as soon as the wedding-train was settled for the night, and tents set up in the field, he went to Styepan's tent and whispered to him: 'O *stari svat*, bridegroom's best man, my friend Styepan, let me spend the night by your charge, the young Bulgarian maiden; just to look at her face I should be happy, and I would reward you by a bootful of ducats.'

Styepan was greatly surprised at this request; he answered sharply: 'Do not talk like this. Be quiet, my Lord Duke; may God turn you into a stone for your sinful thoughts! Do you want to lose your head?'

His words sobered the Duke and he remained quiet, but not for long, though. As they settled for the second night, he walked over to Styepan's white tent and whispered again, more urgently: 'Let me spend the night near the young bride, Styepan, and I shall give you two of my boots full of golden ducats.'

Styepan retorted bitterly: 'Go away, Duke, may God's wrath strike you this very minute! How can you ever nurse thoughts like that about the bride, your *kooma*, who should be more sacred to you than your own sister!'

The Duke returned to his own tent in shame. However, the beautiful face he had glimpsed but for a brief moment made him restless as soon as night fell for the third time.

'Let me be near her, Styepan, and I shall give you three bootfuls of golden ducats,' he almost wailed in his friend's ear, coming into his white tent.

This temptation Styepan could not resist. Dazzled by so much gold, he agreed to let the Venetian have his way. The Duke took the maiden by the hand and led her to his own tent. Coming in, he asked her to sit down and began to speak sweetly to her. As he bent over to kiss her, the Bulgarian maiden exclaimed:

'How can you think of kissing me, Duke of Venice! Do you not know that it is such a terrible sin that the earth would open beneath us and the sky would crush us if we, *koom* and *kooma*, started kissing!'

The Duke only smiled and answered after a while: 'I have done it before, I have kissed many a bride to whom I was *koom* before you and, believe me, the earth never opened, the sky never crushed us and nobody was any the wiser for it! So let me kiss you, fair maiden!' he pleaded urgently, coming close to her.

The bride shrank back again, saying: 'All that may be as you say, my Lord Duke, but my old mother made me swear that I should never kiss a bearded man—I may caress only the clean cheek of a young warrior—such as Kralyevich Marko's.'

Hearing her words, the Duke called the barbers at once, for that at

74

least was something which could easily be put right. The barbers shaved him quickly, and the young bride bowed to him and collected his shorn beard in a handkerchief. The barbers left the tent and the Duke pressed nearer to the maiden again.

'Sit down and let me kiss you, fair maiden,' said the Duke.

'Oh, my *koom*, Duke of Venice, if Marko hears you, we shall both lose our heads,' the bride shied away.

'Do not worry about that, dear maiden—there is Marko, sitting under his tent in the midst of the wedding party. Can't you see his white tent? There is a golden apple with two precious stones on the top of it, shining so brightly that you can see far and wide around it!'

The maiden rose from her cushion and smiled at him: 'Let me, please, go out to see what kind of weather there is tonight—I want to know whether the sky is clear or clouded.'

The Duke let the girl step out, but as soon as she was outside his tent, she ran away on her light young feet and was in Marko's tent in no time. Finding him asleep, his betrothed wept. Marko woke up, startled, and frowned, seeing her in his tent.

'Why did you come here, you heathenish Bulgarian maiden? Do you not know that the old customs do not allow the future bride and bridegroom to be in the same tent together before they have been lawfully wedded in church, as good, faithful Christians?'

In his sudden anger, Marko put his hand on the hilt of his sabre. The maiden bowed low to him.

'I am no heathen, my lord Kralyevich Marko. I am of noble Christian birth, the same as you—which cannot be said for your companions who are heathens indeed! Your *stari svat* sold me to our future *koom* for three bootfuls of golden ducats. In case you do not believe me, Marko, here is the Duke's shorn beard.' She opened her handkerchief and spread the beard before her betrothed.

'Sit down, fair maiden,' said Marko, stretching himself on the rug again. 'Sit down and try to sleep, for I am very weary; I shall see about this in the morning.' Almost before he had uttered these words, Marko fell asleep.

As the sun rose next morning, Marko arose, put his fur-lined surcoat on inside out, as he did whenever he was angry, took the heavy mace in his hand, and walked straight to his *koom* and *stari svat*.

'Good morning, my friends!' he greeted them. 'Where is your charge, my betrothed, Styepan? Where is she, my *koom*, Duke of Venice?'

F

The *stari svat* kept silent, not daring to utter a word, but the Duke of Venice smiled: 'Strange days have come about, Kralyevich Marko, strange days when people are so odd that you cannot even crack a joke safely.'

'A poor joke indeed, Duke of Venice,' said Marko through his clenched teeth. 'Your shorn beard is no joke at all, though! Where is the beard that was on your face yesterday?'

The Duke was about to answer, but Kralyevich Marko did not let him: he drew out his sabre and slew the Duke on the spot.

Meanwhile Styepan ran down the field, fast as lightning, but Kralyevich Marko caught up with him in no time, and cut off his head, too. Having thus settled his account with his unfaithful friends, he returned to his tent, mounted his brave steed, Sharin, and gave a sign to the wedding-suite to start on the last lap of their journey. And indeed, the bridegroom and his bride reached the white town of Prilep on that very day, riding at the head of the festive wedding-train. Marko's old mother was happy and proud as she welcomed them to their white mansion, where many friends were waiting to celebrate Marko's wedding.

KRALYEVICH MARKO AND ALIL-AGA

TWO sworn brothers, Kralyevich Marko and lord Kostadin, were riding in the streets of Constantinople. Marko turned to his good friend: 'My sworn brother, lord Kostadin, I shall pretend to be very ill; seeing me like that maybe somebody will dare to challenge me to a fight. I wish they would, for I feel a little rusty, having lived a quiet life for several days now.'

Saying this, he bent low on his horse Sharats, almost lying on the saddle, and rode on through the crowded streets. Nor for long though, for they soon came face to face with the Sultan's favourite, Alil-Aga, accompanied by thirty retainers.

The Turk reined in his horse and spoke to Marko: 'Brave warrior, Kralyevich Marko, come out to try your luck in archery with me today. Should you win at the contest, I shall give you my white mansion with all that is in it, including my faithful wife. But if I should prove better than you, I do not ask either for your palace or your wife, but shall be content just with hanging you and taking over your brave steed Sharats.'

'Let me alone, you accursed Turk! I am not fit for shooting arrows, for I am ill, very ill with a bad ague. I can hardly sit in my saddle, let alone shoot arrows with you!'

However, the Turk was not to be put off easily and he caught an end of Marko's surcoat. Marko drew out the knife from his belt and cut off the piece of cloth in Alil-Aga's hand. The Turk now caught Sharin's halter with his right hand and Marko's chest with his left.

Blood rushed through Marko's veins and he sat up, all flaring with wrath. He suddenly drew in the reins of his steed. Sharin started prancing madly about, leaping over horses and horsemen. Marko shouted:

'My sworn brother, lord Kostadin, go to my rooms and bring me my Tatar arrow, the one with nine white falcon feathers in it, whilst I go with the Aga to the *Cadi* who will write in court the terms of our shooting contest, so that there shall be no cause afterwards for any quarrel between Alil-Aga and me.'

Kostadin went to Marko's rooms, and Marko rode with Alil-Aga to the Turkish judge, the *Cadi*. As they entered the court room, Alil-Aga took off his slippers, walked to the *Cadi* and, sitting down at his side, discreetly put twelve golden ducats under the judge's knee.

'There, Effendi, there are the ducats for you; do not write a valid testimony of our agreement for Marko,' he whispered.

But Marko knew Turkish, and understood all the Aga said. As he had no ducats with him at the time, he put his heavy mace across his knees:

'Listen to me, you Effendi *Cadi*! Take care you write a valid agreement, for here is my gilded six-knobbed mace: if I should start beating you with it, you will need no herbs to cure you! You will forget all about law and court-trials. As for those ducats, if I were just to touch you gently with this mace, you would soon see the last of them.'

Effendi *Cadi* shook as with a dreadful ague just by looking at Marko's six-knobbed mace and his scowling face; he wrote down the testimony slowly with trembling fingers.

Thereupon the two lords betook themselves to the battlefield, the Aga followed by his thirty retainers, and Marko almost alone but for several Christians, Greeks and Bulgarians who had gathered around him.

'Well, knight, go, shoot your arrow! You boast that you are a fine warrior, and brag to the Sultan and his high dignitaries that you are able to shoot down the eagle flying high up in the sky, leading the clouds in his wake,' said the Turk, jeeringly, when they reached the field.

'True, Turk, I am a brave warrior, but you are entitled to take precedence over me, for yours is the empire and you Turks are the lords now. Besides, you asked me to come and shoot arrows with you, so put in your arrow, Turk, and shoot first.'

The Turk shot his first arrow and far it fell indeed: they measured the distance and found that it had fallen a hundred and twenty arshins away; Marko shot his arrow now, but his fell two hundred arshins from the starting mark. The Turk shot a second arrow—three hundred arshins off, but Marko's second went five hundred arshins from the mark. The third of the Turk's arrows spanned the distance of six hundred arshins. At that moment lord Kostadin came to the field and handed Marko his Tatar arrow, with nine white falcon's feathers in it.

Marko shot his Tatar arrow now and it flew so high, and far, far, so far that nobody could see it, let alone measure the distance to the place where it fell to the ground.

The Turk was so desperate that he began to weep and beseech Marko: 'By God, my sworn brother Marko, by God and by your Saint John, take my white mansion, take my faithful wife and all my other earthly possessions, but do not hang me, for the love of your God and ours, do not hang me, Marko!'

'Oh, you foolish Turk—you make me your sworn brother and in the same breath you give me your wife! I do not need her. Besides, with us Serbs it is not the same as with you Turks: a sister-in-law (as your wife is to me now, since you asked me to be your sworn brother), is the same to any of us as our own dear sisters. I have my faithful wife at home, the noble and virtuous lady Yelitsa.

'I would have forgiven you all you did to me today, but there is just one thing I cannot forgive you: you tore off a wing of my surcoat. Give me three loads of gold to have it patched and I shall forgive you everything.'

The Turkish Aga leapt with joy, embraced Marko and kissed him with gratitude. He took the Serbian Kralyevich to his lordly mansion then and feasted him for three whole days. When the time came for Marko to return to his home, Alil-Aga gave him the three loads of treasure, whereas his wife, now Marko's sworn sister, gave him a gold-embroidered shirt together with a beautiful, costly handkerchief. Then, in order that Kralyevich Marko, noble prince as he was, should travel in state and unmolested, Alil-Aga gave him a retinue numbering three hundred men who saw him safely to his own home.

KRALYEVICH MARKO AND MINA
OF KOSTUR

NE evening, as Marko sat at dinner with his mother
and his wife, Yelitsa, eating bread and drinking his
favourite red wine, messengers brought him three
letters. The first letter was sent by the Turkish
Sultan, Bayazeth, who was summoning Marko to
come and fight at his side against the bitter, dark
soldiers in Arabia; the second came from the Hungarian King in
Budim, inviting Marko to come to his wedding and be his wedding
Koom. The third was from his friend, Yanko of Sibin, who asked Marko
to come and be godfather at the baptism of his two infant sons.

Marko read the three letters and turned to his mother, perplexed:
'Tell me, dear mother, what is my first duty now: should I go with
the Sultan's hosts, to the King's wedding, or to the christening of
Yanko's infant sons?'

'O my son Marko, to go to a wedding means to go to a joyful, gay
occasion; going to the baptism of somebody's children is what old
customs order us to do, but going to join the Sultan's hosts is doubtless
something one *must* do. I therefore advise you to go to the Sultan, for

80

God will certainly have understanding for us and forgive you neglecting your other duties, whereas the Turks would never understand or forget you if you disregarded their summons.'

Kralyevich Marko made his preparations and, before riding out of his castle with his faithful servant Goluban, he took leave of his old mother, and warned her:

'Remember my words, my dear old mother now! Shut the gates of the castle early in the evening, and open them late in the morning; I have quarrelled with the accursed villain, Mina of Kostur, and fear now that he might come and ransack the castle in my absence.'

Thereupon he took leave of his mother and his wife and rode away, with the servant Goluban in his wake.

After the third day's journey, Marko sat down to his supper; Goluban was serving him his food and red wine. Marko took a cup of wine, but sleep suddenly overcame him; the cup fell out of his hand and the red wine spilled all over the table. Goluban shook him by the shoulder.

'Wake up, my lord Kralyevich Marko; you have been to wars before, but you have never fallen asleep like that; never has the full cup dropped out of your hands!'

Startled from his sleep, Marko rubbed his eyes and said to the youth: 'Goluban, my faithful servant, it is a strange dream that I dreamed during this brief spell of sleep: I saw a wisp of fog rise above the castle of Kostur and sail across the sky, increasing greatly, until it enveloped the town of Prilep and my castle in it. Hidden by the dense fog, Mina of Kostur ransacked my castle, took everything away, and set fire to the despoiled fortress, taking with him my faithful wife and trampling with his horsemen over my poor old mother. He also led away all the horses from my stables and emptied my treasury.'

His servant Goluban comforted Marko: 'Do not fear, Kralyevich Marko; being a brave, adventurous warrior you had a dream befitting your nature. Dreams are just idle lies, and God is the only truth on this earth.'

Somewhat comforted by these words, Marko continued his journey until at last he reached Constantinople. Soon after his arrival, the Sultan raised his numerous, powerful hosts and sailed with them across the deep-blue sea to the rebellious Arabian lands. The Sultan's army took one town after another until the number of the vanquished cities rose to forty-five. But when they came to the city of Kara-Okan,

81

their warriors' luck changed. They set siege to the city and tried by means of all tactics they could think of to conquer it, but the city firmly resisted all their attacks for three whole years.

Meanwhile, violent battles were fought outside the city; violent battles in which Marko slew many a well-known Arab champion. Whenever he did so he cut off his head and took it to the Sultan who, greatly pleased by his prowess, always rewarded him richly.

The Turkish warriors grew envious of Marko: they could not bear the thought that a miscreant (as they called Christians and all those whose religion was other than Islamic) should rise so high in their own Sultan's esteem, and, what is more, become so rich by it. They therefore said to the Sultan one day:

'Our lord Sultan Bayazeth, Marko is not the hero you think: he cuts off the heads of warriors who have already been slain, and brings them to you as his own trophies, expecting your generous reward.'

Kralyevich Marko soon learned about their slander and went to the Sultan, as if he had no inkling of it.

'My lord Sultan, my foster-father, tomorrow is Saint George's day, my patron saint's day, which I wish to celebrate according to our old Serbian customs. Give me leave to absent myself from the battle-field and let me take with me my sworn brother Alil-Aga, for I wish to celebrate and feast in his company.'

The Sultan could not refuse Marko's request. He let him go to the mountains, to celebrate his patron saint's day in the company of his sworn brother, Alil-Aga.

The two warriors went some distance from the Sultan's hosts, pitched their white tent in a pleasant clearing in the woods, and started to drink the dark-red wine which the faithful servant Goluban had brought with them, and was handing them, cup after cup.

However, as soon as daylight came, the Arab watchmen noticed that Marko was no longer in their enemy's ranks.

'Charge and attack for all you are worth, you fierce Arabs! The terrible knight on the big piebald horse is not with the Turks today!' they shouted to their warriors. Their words had such an effect that the Arabs charged like a mighty hurricane and slew thirty thousand of the Sultan's soldiers.

Greatly worried by the day's losses, the Sultan hastily dispatched a letter to Marko: 'Hurry back, my foster-son Marko! I have lost thirty thousand soldiers today!'

82

Marko perused the letter over a cup of wine and wrote back: 'Why, what need is there for such hurry, my lord Sultan and foster-father! I have hardly drunk any wine yet, let alone risen to my feet to give homage to my patron saint as our customs require me to do!'

The Arab watchmen shouted on the second morning again: 'Charge and attack, you fierce Arabs! The fearful knight on the big piebald horse is not in our enemy's ranks today!'

The Arabs attacked for all they were worth again, and as the consequence of their ardour, the Sultan lost sixty thousand warriors.

'Hurry back, my foster-son Marko! I have lost sixty thousand men today!' wrote the Sultan sending his fastest Tatar to the mountain.

'Wait a little, my lord Sultan and foster-father! I have not yet feasted my friends and servants according to our old customs,' were Marko's words in answer to the summons. He stayed on in the mountain clearing, enjoying his wine and his friends' company.

How glad the Arab watchmen were when they discovered that on the third morning Marko was still missing from the Turkish side!

'Charge and attack, you fierce Arabs!' they shouted from the top of their high posts, imparting to their army once more the good news.

Encouraged by their two previous victories, the Arabs swept like a gale across a field, turning it into a desert in no time. A hundred thousand Turks fell on that day and the Sultan almost wailed writing to Marko: 'Come back in all haste, my foster-son, Marko! Come back, hurry to your foster-father quickly! The Arabs are almost at the door of my tent and I am in great peril myself!'

Only then did Marko mount his horse Sharats. On the third evening he rode back to join the Sultan's hosts.

Next morning the enemy's watchmen cried, piercing the air: 'Now retreat, you fierce Arabs! The fearful knight on the big piebald horse is on the field again!'

Marko charged among the Arabs and in no time divided their hosts into three parts: one of them he slew with his mighty sabre, the other he destroyed trampling over it with his brave Sharats, and the third part he drove to the Sultan's tent where they were all captured as slaves. But that brave exploit cost Marko seventy wounds which he won in fighting the Arabs. As he came into the Sultan's tent, he fell on the cushions, his body leaning partly over the Sultan's knees.

'My foster-son Marko, are your wounds mortal? Or do you think you will recover from them? Shall I send for doctors and medicines to cure you?' the Sultan asked, worried about his most valiant knight.

'I do not think my wounds are mortal, Sultan, my foster-father, and I believe that they can be cured.'

The Sultan took a thousand ducats out of his pockets and gave them to Marko to find a doctor who would heal his wounds. He ordered two servants to stay at Marko's side, fearing the worst.

However, Marko did not even ask for a doctor: instead he went from one inn to another, trying to find the inn which sold the best wine. After tasting the wine in many places, he found some to his liking in one of the inns, and sat down to drink. When he had drunk his fill, the wounds were healed, but he was not allowed to enjoy his good health for long. A letter brought him sad news from Prilep: his castle was ransacked and burnt, his old mother had met her death under the robbers' horses, and his faithful wife was enslaved.

Kralyevich Marko went back to the Sultan and complained: 'My lord Sultan, my foster-father, my white castle has been plundered, my dear old mother murdered, my wife enslaved, and all my treasures taken by Mina of Kostur.'

'Do not despair, Marko my foster-son,' said the Sultan, wishing to comfort him; 'if your castle has been burnt, I shall have another one built for you, next to my own palace. It shall be as big and beautiful as my own. If your treasury has been ransacked, I shall make you my tax-collector and you will soon be richer than you ever were; if your wife has been taken away, I shall find another, better one for you.'

'Thank you, Sultan, my foster-father, but when your masons start building a new palace for me, all the poor will curse me, saying, "Look at that Kralyevich Marko! His old castle has burnt down; may his new one be deserted with not a soul in it!" As for your offering to make me your tax-collector, I would not be able to collect any taxes unless I pressed hard on the poor and humble who would then curse me again: "Look at that Kralyevich Marko! The treasures he once had have been taken away from him; may his new ones remain without him, their owner, or any heir of his!' And why should you want to find another wife for me when my own wife still lives? I do not want any of this, but I beg you, my lord, give me three hundred soldiers, *yanicharis*, arm them with small curved scythes, and give them light picks. I shall take them to the white castle of Kostur and shall try to win my wife back.'

84

The Sultan heard his plea and gave him the three hundred *yanicharis*, armed as Marko requested.

'Listen, brothers, *yanicharis* of the Sultan, go now to the Greek town of Kostur. When the Greeks see you, they will rejoice, saying, "What good fortune! There are workmen who will hoe our vineyards cheaply!" Do not listen to them, my dear brothers, but go straight to the castle of Kostur, surround it, and drink wine and brandy until I arrive there too.'

The *yanicharis* obeyed their new master and went to the town of Kostur. Marko, meanwhile, rode to Mount Athos where he confessed his sins and received the holy communion. He was forgiven for having shed so much blood in his lifetime. His sins absolved, he was ready to go to the town of Kostur, but before departing he donned the black robes of a monk, and let his black beard grow. It grew very fast and soon it was falling down over his chest. On his head he put a monk's tall cap, and, thus dressed, he threw himself on his Sharin's back and rode to Kostur.

Presenting himself at the gate as a monk, Marko had no difficulty in being received by the servants and ushered into the chamber where Mina sat, drinking wine. Marko's own wife was serving him.

'Tell me truthfully, you black monk, how did you come to own that piebald steed?' Mina asked, eyeing the horse through the window.

'I have been with the Sultan's hosts in the Arab lands, my lord Mina; there was a big fool by the name of Kralyevitch Marko with us too. He fell in a battle there and I buried him, performing all my Christian duties over his grave, and that is why I have been given his horse.'

Mina leapt to his feet joyfully. 'Well done, black monk!' he exclaimed. 'For a long time now I have been expecting such good news: I have ransacked Marko's castle, ransacked and burnt it to ashes, and I have taken his wife and brought her hither, but I could not take her for my wedded wife whilst Marko was still alive. I have been waiting for him to fall in one of his many battles, and now, since he is no more among us, you shall perform the wedding rites and marry me and his wife.'

Marko took a prayer-book out of his pocket and performed the wedding rites, thus marrying Mina to his own wife!

After the wedding they sat down to feast and rejoice. Mina turned to his wife: 'Listen, Yela, my sweetheart! So far you have been Marko's wife, but henceforth you are Mina's beloved. Go down, my dear wife, go to my treasury in the vaulted cellar and bring three cupfuls of ducats, for I want to reward this black monk.'

85

Yela went down and brought back three cupfuls of ducats, but she carefully took them not from Mina's chest, but from that in which Marko's plundered treasures were stored. With the gold, she handed the monk also a sabre, rusty with lying idle in the damp cellar.

'Take this too, black monk, take it and pray for the peace of Kralyevich Marko's soul.'

Marko took the sabre and looked at it thoughtfully, turning it in his hands.

'My lord Mina of Kostur, may I dance on this joyful occasion? Would it be seemly to execute a monk's gay dance here?' he asked, looking up, his dark eyes glittering.

'Yes, of course you may; why should that be unseemly?' answered Mina.

Marko jumped up to his light feet and quickly turned about two or three times. The whole tower shook beneath him. He suddenly drew the rusty sabre out of its sheath, swung it around and chopped off Mina's head.

'Advance now, my good *yanicharis*! There is no more Mina of Kostur!'

The *yanicharis* charged on the castle, ransacked it in no time, and finally set it on fire. Marko, meanwhile, had taken out of the cellar his own treasure and that belonging to Mina, and was now on his way home with his faithful wife. He rode back to Prilep with a light heart, singing happily.

KRALYEVICH MARKO AND
THE ARAB

 BLACK Arab had a castle with a high tower built by the sea. When the building was finished, the Arab had glass put in all the windows; he had all the floors covered by costly rugs and the walls hung with silk and velvet. Looking at his new castle and pacing up and down the silent rooms, he spoke to it:

'What is the good of you, here by the sea, my lovely tall tower? What is the good when there is no one to live in you? I have no mother or sister, and I have not married yet, so I have no wife either to walk upon your soft carpets. But, may I not be the Arab I am if I do not ask the Sultan to give me his daughter in marriage! He will have to give her to me, or to come out to the battlefield and fight with me!'

No sooner said than done! The Arab sat in one of his quiet, empty rooms and wrote a letter to the Sultan.

87

'My lord Sultan of Constantinople, I have had a castle built with a high tower by the blue sea; there is nobody to walk in it, nobody but me. Give me your daughter to be my wife, my lord. If you refuse, come out to fight a battle with me!'

When the letter reached the Sultan, he inquired for someone to stand as his champion, promising great wealth and riches of all kinds to him who would slay the black Arab. Many youths went to try their luck, but none of them was seen in Constantinople ever again.

The Sultan grew worried, as time went by; not only was the Arab still alive, but many of the Sultan's best knights and warriors had perished fighting with him. Even that was not the worst, for something even more terrible happened before long.

One day the black Arab put on his best costly clothes, hung his sharp sabre on his belt, prepared his grey mare, putting golden reins on her, folded his tent and tied it to the saddle behind him. He hung his heavy mace on the saddle, and, taking his dangerous spear, mounted his steed and rode straight to Constantinople. Reaching the city gate, the Arab stuck his spear in the ground, tethered his mare to it, and pitched his tent. He then sent word to the Sultan's city, saying that the citizens were to give him every night a good sheep, a cartful of white bread, a barrel of hot brandy and two of red wine; also, a fair young maiden to serve him. If they did not do his bidding, a worse evil would soon befall them.

Before long he grew very rich, for he sold to Italy all he did not need for himself. Even that was not the worst, as they soon realized. The mighty Arab, dizzy with power, mounted his slender grey mare again and rode into the white city of Constantinople, straight to the Sultan's palace. He stopped in front of it and shouted:

'Bring out your daughter, Sultan of Constantinople! Bring out your daughter and give her to me!'

He then threw his heavy mace at the Sultan's windows and broke all the glass in them.

Seeing that there was nobody to fight for him now, the Sultan agreed shamefully to give him his daughter in marriage.

'I shall return in a fortnight,' said the Arab, 'for I must go back to my castle on the gentle coastland and collect my friends and guests for the wedding.'

He rode home happily, whilst the young maiden, learning what the future had in store for her, started to wail and cry bitterly. Her mother,

88

the Sultaniya, tried to comfort her, but without much success. She fell asleep at last. In her dream she saw a man who spoke thus to her:

'There is a wide field in your Empire, my lady Sultaniya, and in that wide Field of Kossovo there is the town of Prilep, where Kralyevich Marko lives. They say that Marko is a brave, valiant knight. Send him a letter, my lady Sultaniya; ask him to be your son by God, promise him a rich reward and call him hither to save your daughter from the black Arab.'

As soon as she awoke, the Sultaniya ran to the Sultan's chamber and told him of her dream. The Sultan quickly took a quill-pen and wrote at once to Kralyevich Marko:

'Be by God my son, Kralyevich Marko; come to my white city of Constantinople and slay my foe, the black Arab, to save my fair daughter. I shall give you three loads of treasure.'

When Kralyevich Marko read the epistle, he said to the Tatar who had brought it:

'Go back, Tatar of the Sultan! Give my greetings to the Sultan, my foster-father, and tell him I dare not fight with the Arab. He is known as the best fighter there is in this country, and when he cuts off my head what good are the three loads of treasure to me?'

The Tatar rode back on his swift horse and repeated Marko's words to the Sultan.

The Sultaniya thought for a while and, believing that she would move him by her plea, sent him her own letter this time:

'By God, my son Kralyevich Marko, do not let my dear daughter marry the black Arab! I shall give you five loads of treasure.'

Marko perused the letter and said, shaking his head, to the Tatar: 'Go back, Tatar of the Sultan, go back and tell my foster-mother that I dare not fight with the Arab. He is the best warrior in this vast Empire and will cut off my head. And I, tell her, Tatar, I prefer my own head to all the Sultan's treasure.'

Back went the Tatar and reported Marko's message. Hearing him, the fair maiden ran to her room, took a sharp quill and wrote a letter with her own blood instead of ink:

'My sworn brother, Kralyevich Marko, I beseech you by God and by your Saint John to be a true brother to me. Do not give me to the black Arab! I shall give you seven loads of treasure, seven fine shirts, embroidered with golden thread; I shall also give you a golden dish encircled by a golden snake which holds its head high; in its mouth the snake holds a precious stone which shines so brightly that midnight is as bright as noon when you eat your supper by its light. I shall also give you a beautifully wrought sabre with three golden hilts, each of them adorned by a precious stone. That sabre alone is worth three of the Sultan's big cities. Moreover, I shall have a seal made on it so that no Vizier or other high dignitary can slay you before asking his lord, the illustrious Sultan, whether he may do so.'

The Tatar carried the third letter to Marko. 'Woe to me, my sworn sister! It is bad to go where you ask me to, but it is worse to remain here,' Marko mused after reading her words. 'If I fear not the Sultan and the Sultaniya, I do fear God and Saint John. Go I will; whether I come back or not does not matter to me any longer.'

He gave no message to the Tatar, but as soon as the Sultan's messenger was gone he climbed up his tower, put on his riding clothes, and on top of them a jacket made of wolf skins; on his head he wore a fur cap, made of wolfskin too. Marko then took his sabre and spear, saddled his valiant Sharats, and hung a sheepskin full of wine on the right side of his saddle, the heavy mace on the left, to keep balance, and then jumped on to Sharin's back and rode straight to the white city of Constantinople.

Reaching it, Kralyevich Marko did not go to pay homage to the Sultan or any of his Viziers. He stopped instead at the New Inn and, after telling the innkeeper to prepare a room for him, he took his horse to the nearby lake to let him drink cool, fresh water. But the horse seemed unwilling to drink, although he must have been thirsty; yet he would not go back either and kept restlessly glancing around.

After a while a young Turkish maiden walked slowly to the edge of the lake. She bowed humbly to the quiet green waters and spoke, without lifting the gold-embroidered veil from her face:

'God be with you, you cool green lake! God bless you, my eternal home! Henceforth it is here that I shall dwell, for I shall be your bride, my green lake, rather than marry the black Arab.'

'What misfortune drives you to this lake, unknown Turkish lady?' Kralyevich Marko asked, stepping up to her.

'Let me alone, you poor dervish! Why do you ask me when no help can ever come from you?'

Yet her misery was weighing so heavily on her heart that she had to tell him her sad story from the beginning. 'And as a last resource I wrote to Kralyevich Marko, whom many praised as one of the most valiant knights of our Empire, hoping that he would free me from the black Arab! I even pledged him to be my sworn brother, but he neither came nor sent any answer. May he never return to his mother, where-ever he may be at this hour!' she ended with a heavy sigh.

'Do not curse me, my sworn sister! I am Kralyevich Marko.'

The Turkish maiden ran to him and folded her white arms round his neck, imploring him:

'My sworn brother, Kralyevich Marko, do not let me be married to the black Arab!'

'Do not fear him whilst I am alive, sworn sister. I shall not let you be married to the black Arab,' Marko promised. 'Go back to your palace, but do not say a word about me to anyone except your parents, the Sultan and the Sultaniya. Ask them to send me something for dinner, and remind them not to stint on the wine,' he said, feeling his throat go dry with thirst. He mused, looking at her, and said:

'When the Arab comes, welcome him and his wedding-train as you would any other bridegroom. Tell your parents to let you go away with him, so that there shall be no fight in the palace. As for me, I know where and how to welcome him.'

The young maiden returned home contented, and Marko rode back to the New Inn. A princely dinner was brought in before long, with the best wines from the Sultan's own cellars. Marko sat down, enjoy-ing himself after the long journey. He was drinking cup after cup of the heavy red wine, looking out at the passers-by. Suddenly, the innkeeper hurried to the door and shut the inn.

'Why are you shutting your inn so early?' Marko asked, surprised.

'To tell you the truth, unknown warrior, we are all shutting our doors early this evening, for fear of the Arab who has forced our Sultan to give him his daughter in marriage. The hateful bridegroom arrives tonight, and that is why we want to be safe within our homes.'

Marko firmly ordered him to let the door stay open, wishing to see the Arab and his wedding-train. After a while the whole town re-sounded with shrill pipes, and the walls shuddered with the beating of many drums. Into the town rode the Arab on his slender grey mare, followed by five hundred black Arabs, his wedding-suite. The mare was prancing madly along the streets, and stones flew from under her hoofs, breaking many a window and door in the merchant quarter.

As the Arab entered the street where Marko was, he stopped in front of the New Inn, amazed.

'Isn't this a great wonder!' he exclaimed. 'All the doors of Constantinople are shut for fear of me; only this inn stayed open! Is there nobody in it? Or is there some foolish youth sitting inside who never yet heard of me?'

But he was eager to reach the palace and so he did not go in to inquire. He spent the night with his suite in luxurious rooms, hardly able to sleep with impatience. In the morning the Sultan led his daughter from her rooms and gave her to the Arab. Horses were saddled again; there were many more leaving the palace than there had been coming in the previous night: twelve packhorses were loaded with treasure the Sultan had given his son-in-law, and several others were carrying chests with the bride's dowry.

The wedding-train rode past the New Inn again and the Arab could not bridle his curiosity any longer. He stopped and, looking in, saw Marko sitting all by himself in the middle of the inn, drinking red wine not out of cups, but out of a big basin! He would drink half of it himself and give the other half to his horse Sharats.

The Arab was willing to pick a quarrel, but Sharats barred his way and did not let him enter the inn.

The Arab bridegroom returned to his wedding-suite and they all rode through Constantinople in state, with the music louder and shriller and the drums wilder than ever before.

Kralyevich Marko now arose, put on his fur-lined jacket, turning it inside out, drew the fur cap lower on to his brow, hung the wineskin and the mace on the saddle once more, and mounted his Sharats. He reached the wedding-suite soon after they had left Constantinople and he started to quarrel and fight with them; those at the rear ran madly ahead, past the head of the wedding-suite. Marko was now near the fair maiden; he hit with his mace the two young men at her sides, and they both fell off their horses, never to rise again.

The bridegroom was some distance ahead of the others, but a swift youth galloped up to him.

'I have bad news for you, black Arab! A strange knight rode in among your wedding-suite: his horse is unlike any other horse— piebald like a cow rather than a horse, and he himself looks frightening, with his wolfskin coat, his furry cap, and terrible black moustache. The moment he reached us he started dealing blows right and left, making way for himself. Whoever was touched by his mace is not likely to see daylight ever again. He slew the two knights who were guarding your bride, unfortunate black Arab!'

92

The Arab turned his mare round and reined her in only when he was face to face with Marko.

'Bad luck to you, unknown warrior!

'What devil told you to ride among my suite and slay my two best men? Are you such a fool as to know nothing about me? Are you powerful and has your power turned your head? Or are you sick of your life?' the Arab hissed and, after drawing a deep breath, went on:

'I give you my word of honour now, I shall pull in the reins of my mare, shall leap over you seven times, and shall then cut off your head.'

'Do not boast foolishly, you black Arab! If God and good luck will so, you will not leap near me, let alone over me!' said Marko.

The Arab drew the reins in furiously, whipped his mare's flank and was about to leap over Marko, but the brave Sharats stood up on his hind legs, hit the mare with his front legs and she landed, neighing fiercely.

Oh, if one could have stood there and watched the two brave warriors rushing at each other! They were of equal strength and prowess and neither of them could break the other. Their steeds pranced, sabres clanked, spears flew, and the air was full of the din of battle for nearly four hours. At last the Arab realized that Marko was still as fresh as he had been at the beginning of their fight, whereas he himself felt weariness stealing upon him. He rushed back through the city gate, into the merchant quarter of Constantinople. Marko spurred his Sharats, but the mare was swifter, swift as a mountain Vila. She nearly saved the Arab, but Marko remembered his mace, swung it once or twice and hurled it at the Arab. The mace hit him between the shoulder blades and the Arab fell off his horse. Marko ran to him, cut off his head, and led the mare back through the city gate.

He found the Princess alone on the road waiting for him, surrounded by the packhorses loaded with treasure and her dowry. All the Arabs from the wedding-party had disappeared and there was not a trace of them on the road, except the marks their horses had left in the dust.

Kralyevich Marko took the maiden back to the Sultan, her father. 'Here is your fair daughter, my lord Sultan, and there are your packhorses loaded with treasure and with her dowry.'

Saying this, Kralyevich Marko departed from Constantinople without further ado, eager to return to his white city of Prilep.

The next morning, however, the Sultan had seven horses loaded with gold and jewels; his daughter packed the seven gold-embroidered shirts, the golden dish with the snake holding a precious, shining stone in its mouth, and, most precious of all, the fine sharp sabre with three golden hilts and the Sultan's seal, warning everybody, whoever he might be, that its owner was not to be slain without special permission from the Sultan in person. All this was sent to Kralyevich Marko, and with it the Sultan's message:

'Here is some gold for you, Marko. When you have spent it all, come to your foster-father to ask for more, Marko.'

KRALYEVICH MARKO ABOLISHES
THE WEDDING-TAX

NE day, early in the morning, Kralyevich Marko rode down the vast Field of Kossovo. As he came to a river, he saw a maiden coming his way. He stopped and greeted her: 'God be with you, maiden of Kossovo!'

The maiden bowed low and said in answer: 'May God grant you good health, unknown warrior.'

Marko looked closely at her and wondered aloud. 'My dear sister, maiden of Kossovo, how beautiful you must have been when you were younger! What a fine figure and proud bearing you have; how rosy your cheeks are, and what a noble look in your eyes! But your grey hair spoils your looks, for you are certainly still not as old as all that! What has happened to you that your hair should have turned grey so early? Has a misfortune befallen you, your mother or your old father, fair maiden of Kossovo?'

Tears ran down the maiden's rosy cheeks before she answered Kralyevich Marko. 'No personal misfortune has befallen either me or my dear parents, my dear brother, oh unknown warrior, but it is nine years now since an Arab has come from across the sea and taken lease of the Field of Kossovo, granted to him by the Turkish Sultan. He it is who makes us all unhappy, for we all have to provide for his meals, his drinks, and all sorts of whims. Moreover, he decreed that all those who want to be married must pay for it: maidens, future brides, must give thirty golden ducats, and bridegrooms thirty-four. Those who are rich enough give him their ducats, and they alone can be married. As for me, my brothers are poor and, try as we might, we could never scrape enough money together for me or my brothers to marry; that is why I could not have a home and a family of my own, and that is what makes me unhappy. Still, I would not regret that so much— his not letting us young people be married as we would like to—were it not for yet another, worse misfortune: the Arab has ordered his men to bring him a maiden each evening. After spending the night with her, he gives her over to his servants and many of our good maidens have had to obey that hateful order. It is my turn tonight. I do not know what to do now, and I am trying to make up my mind between jumping into the river and drowning, or hanging myself. I much prefer to die, oh brother, than to be a mistress to my country's most bitter enemy.'

Having heard her woes, Kralyevich Marko said: 'My dear sister, maiden of Kossovo, do not, in the name of God, do anything so rash and senseless. Do not burden your soul with such a heavy sin! You should just tell me where the Arab's mansion is, for I wish to speak to him.'

'Why are you asking about the Arab's mansion—may it soon become deserted and empty as wasteland!—my dear brother, unknown champion? Have you found a bride for yourself? Are you taking the tax to him now? You might be your mother's only son and you might perish there! What would your poor, lonely mother do then?'

Marko took thirty golden ducats out of his pocket and handed them to the maiden. 'Take these ducats, my dear sister, and go back to your white home; eat well and take care of yourself, waiting for the bridegroom whom fate has decreed for you. Only show me now where the Arab's mansion is, for I shall pay your wedding-tax for you. Why should the Arab kill me when I have money enough to buy the whole Field of Kossovo, let alone pay my wedding-tax?'

'He has no mansion, dear brother; he and his servants live in tents. Look down the Field of Kossovo now; can you see the silken flag flapping in the breeze? That is the black Arab's tent. It is surrounded by a green lawn, but it is a sad and unhappy lawn, covered with Serbs' heads stuck on the poles. A whole week has not yet gone by from the day the Arab slew seventy-seven unfortunate bridegrooms-to-be from Kossovo. The Arab is accompanied by forty servants who guard him day and night and watch like eagles all who approach him.'

Marko waved to the maiden and rode down the field, causing his good Sharats to be very angry: live flames leapt from under his hoofs and blue fire issued out of his nostrils. Angry was Marko too, riding down the field and, shedding tears down his manly face, he spoke wrathfully:

'Woe to you, unhappy Field of Kossovo, woe to you that you should have lived to see this—that Arabs should rule over you after our honourable Tsar Lazar! I cannot bear the shame, nor stand such dreadful grief as this when I think of the Arabs doing such evil deeds here and kissing our young maidens and newly wed brides!

'I shall revenge you today, my brothers, revenge or die, I promise!' Marko shouted angrily, but there was nobody to hear him.

As he approached the tents, the Arab's sentry saw him and said to his master: 'Oh, my master, lord from across the sea, there is a strange knight riding down the Field of Kossovo, a strange knight and a piebald horse yet stranger, with live flames leaping from under his hoofs and blue fire issuing out of his nostrils. It looks as if he is going to attack us!'

'My children, my forty brave servants, the knight will not dare to attack us,' said the black Arab, smiling. 'He has probably found a sweetheart and is bringing his wedding-tax to me; he may be angry because he is sorry to part with his golden ducats. Go out, brave servants. Give him a fine welcome in front of our pleasant lawn: bow low to him and receive his horse and arms as he dismounts. Usher him then into the tent to me: I shall not take his gold but shall behead him, in order to gain a horse which befits *me* better than him.'

The Arab's servants hastened out to obey their master's orders, but when they saw Marko at a few paces' distance, they scurried back under the tent, frightened, trying to hide behind their master, and covering their sabres beneath their cloaks so that he should not see them.

Marko rode into the enclosure alone, dismounted his horse in front of the tent, and said: 'You walk up and down this paddock, Sharats, whilst I go in to see the Arab, but do not go far from the entrance of the tent in case I should need you.'

Marko walked into the tent; he saw the Arab sitting and drinking the cool wine, handed to him by a maiden and a young woman.

'God help you, my dear lord,' said Marko by way of greeting.

'God be with you, unknown champion! Come, sit down and drink some wine with me. Later on you might, perhaps, tell me what has brought you here,' the Arab answered courteously.

'I have no time for drinking wine with you, my lord. As for my business with you, it is a good one, so good that it could hardly be better: I have a betrothed and am now going to fetch her, and go to the church to be married to her. My wedding-guests are down the road waiting for me, and I have just come in to give you my wedding-tax, so that no one shall be able to stand in my way. Tell me, how much am I to give you for my wedding?'

'You know it only too well, I presume: a bride pays thirty ducats and the bridegroom pays thirty-four. As for you, who are obviously a remarkable champion, you might easily give me a whole hundred!'

Marko reached into his pocket, took three golden ducats out of it, and threw them in front of the Arab.

'This is all I now have, believe me. If you will wait a little, I shall bring you all the fine gifts I receive, according to our old customs, from my bride's parents. You will have the gifts, and I my fair bride.'

'I am not prepared to wait for your money and you should know it, you scoundrel!' hissed the Arab like a venomous snake. 'Not only do you refuse to give me my due, but you dare try to sneer at me!' he roared, swinging his heavy mace and hitting Marko three or four times with it.

Marko burst out laughing: 'Are you joking or hitting me seriously, you black champion?'

'I am not joking. Can't you see that I am utterly serious?' the Arab hissed back furiously.

'And I was thinking that you were only joking!' said Marko. 'I also have some kind of a mace, and I shall now touch you lightly three or four times—just to make the score even; afterwards we shall go out and fight the real battle on the field.'

Marko swung his mace and struck the Arab but his touch was so light that the Arab's head was severed from his body. Marko looked down, laughing:

'Praise be to God, for all His mercy! How swiftly did his head fall off—almost as if it had never sat on his shoulders!'

He drew his sabre now and slew the servants, all but four. Those he let go, to tell the world how it was with Marko and the Arab. He took all the Serbs' heads off the poles and buried them so that the eagles and ravens should not harm them. The poles were now carrying Arabs' heads.

Marko ordered the four remaining servants to go and herald the good news all over the Field of Kossovo.

'Where there is a young maiden who has reached the marriageable age, let her look for a bridegroom, and let her get married whilst she is still fair and young.

'Where there is a young man, let him look for a bride and let them marry in peace, for there is no more wedding-tax to be paid now.

'Marko has paid it for all of them, once for all time.'

Thanksgiving was heard from young and old alike: 'May God grant long life to Marko who saved his country from a sad fate and slew the villain! May both his soul and body rest in peace!'

KRALYEVICH MARKO AND MUSSA
KESSEDZHIYA

USSA, the Albanian Turk, was drinking wine in a
Constantinople inn. After a while he said, drunk with
too much wine:

'It is nine years now that I have been serving our
Sultan in Constantinople, and yet I have not been
given a horse and arms or any clothes, either new
ones or old. I have had enough of this. I give you my word of honour,'
he said, turning to his friends, 'that I shall go down to the coast and
become an outlaw: I shall close the roads and ways to my castle and
build a tall tower with gallows underneath. All the Sultan's men who
come my way shall be hanged.'

What the Turk declared when drunk, he accomplished later, when
he was sober: he went to the coast and closed all the roads and ways
leading from the coastland to the Sultan's town, the roads along which
three hundred packs of treasure were carried every year. All the gold
and treasure which by right belonged to other people or to the Sultan,
Mussa now captured and kept for himself. Moreover, he had all the
Sultan's dignitaries who happened to pass his way hanged beneath
his tower.

The Sultan received complaints about this behaviour from all sides,
and he finally decided to put an end to Mussa's robbery by sending his
own Vizier, Chuprilich, at the head of three thousand soldiers to
restore peace and order in the coastland.

However, the result was disastrous: most of the Sultan's soldiers fell
in the battle, and the Vizier was captured by Mussa, who sent him

to the Sultan, his hands tied behind his back and his feet bound under his horse, to tell him what happened.

The Sultan was fuming with rage now: he started to look for a brave man who would slay Mussa, and promised unheard-of rewards to him who should prove successful in the exploit. Many were tempted, and they rode down to the coastland, but none of them returned.

The Sultan was greatly disturbed. Seeing him downcast and desperate, the Vizier Chuprilich said to him: 'My lord Sultan, if Kralyevich Marko were here now, he is the only one who could slay Mussa.'

The Sultan looked at him angrily, hardly managing to withold his tears. 'Let me alone, my Vizier! Why do you have to mention Kralyevich Marko to me! Don't you know that his bones must have turned to rot and dust by this time! Three years ago I threw him into a dungeon—and I have not opened the door of it since. He must have been dead long ago.'

'What would you give to him who told you Kralyevich Marko was alive, my gracious lord?' the Vizier asked.

'What! I would give him Bosnia to rule over for nine years, without paying me a farthing in taxes or anything else,' the Sultan said wistfully.

The Vizier leapt to his feet and ran down to the dark dungeon. He opened the door and, taking out Kralyevich Marko, led him into the Sultan's presence. Marko was a strange sight to behold, no doubt: his hair was so long that it fell down to the ground (for while he had been in prison, he was wont to lie upon one half of it, using the other half as a covering over his body); his nails were so long that he could easily have ploughed the soil with them. The damp, cold dungeon had made his face dark and sallow, and he was a sad sight if there ever was one, thought the Sultan.

'Are you alive, Marko?' the Sultan asked him, hardly believing his eyes.

'I am, my lord Sultan, but am not well at all,' Marko answered him.

The Sultan asked him to sit down and listen to his tale of woe. When he had finished, he asked:

'Could you go to the coastland now, Marko, could you go there and slay Mussa? I would give you all you could wish for if you would put an end to the villain.'

'No, my lord Sultan, I cannot do so now! The damp and cold dungeon has almost deprived me of my sight. I can hardly see now, let alone fight a battle with Mussa! Let me stay for a while in one of the

Constantinople inns; give me plenty of wine, brandy, good mutton, and white bread. After some time I shall let you know whether I am fit for battle or not.'

The Sultan summoned three young barbers: one of them washed Marko's face and cut his hair, the other shaved him, and the third cut and trimmed his nails. He was then taken to an inn, with, at his elbow, wine, brandy, meat, and bread, of which he might eat and drink as much as he wished. Marko spent three months there and the Sultan called him one day again:

'Could you trust yourself to go to the coastland now, Marko? I am weary with listening to all the unfortunate people complaining of the accursed Mussa.'

'Give me dry wood which has been lying in the attic for nine years, my lord Sultan; only then shall I see whether I am fit or not.'

The Sultan had such wood brought down from his attic. Marko took it into his right hand and pressed it hard: the wood broke into two or three pieces, but not a drop of water came out of it.

'In truth, my lord Sultan, the time has not yet come,' Marko said and walked out. Another month went by and Marko spent his days at the inn, much as before, eating and drinking. When he felt his old strength returning, he asked for the dry wood to be brought to him again. The servants rushed to the attic and fetched it for him: Marko pressed the wood in his right hand and it broke into two or three pieces, but, also, two drops of water fell out of it.

'The time has come for the fight, my lord Sultan,' Marko said, and he walked to Novak the smith.

'Forge a sabre for me, Novak the smith, forge a sabre better than any one you have ever yet forged!' He gave the smith thirty golden ducats and went to another inn, to wait for his sabre. After three or four days he returned to Novak.

'Is my sabre ready for me, smith Novak?'

The smith brought it out of his workshop and gave it to Marko. Kralyevich Marko looked at it, 'Is it good, smith Novak?'

'There is the sabre and there is the anvil, Marko—try it and you will see what it is like,' Novak answered in a low voice.

Marko swung the sabre in his right hand and hit the iron anvil, cutting it in two.

'Tell me truly, Novak the smith, have you ever made a better one?'

'I shall truly answer you, Kralyevich Marko: indeed I have forged a better one, for a warrior better than you. When Mussa decided to go back to his coastland I made a sabre for him and when he hit the anvil, he cut in two not only the anvil, but also the stone underneath.'

This angered Marko so much that he cut off Novak's arm, saying: 'There now, Novak the smith, this is for you so that you shall never forge another sabre, better or worse than this one. And here are a hundred golden ducats to support you for the rest of your life.'

He then mounted on his Sharin's back and rode down to the gentle coastland, inquiring for Mussa all the time.

Early one morning Marko was riding up a narrow mountain gorge when whom should he see riding towards him but Mussa himself; his legs crossed on his horse, he was throwing his mace up in the sky and catching it in his hands as it fell back, just for amusement. As they came face to face, Marko said:

'Make way for me, Mussa of Albania; make way or pay due respect to me!'

'Go by, Marko, and do not seek to quarrel with me, Marko, or better, dismount your horse and come to drink wine with me, for I shall not make way for you. You may well have been borne by a Queen in a King's palace on soft mattresses, you may well have been wrapped in pure silk and linen with golden thread woven in it, you may well have been fed on honey and sugar; as for me, a bitter Albanian woman gave life to me, lying on a cold stone by her sheep; she wrapped me in rough, black cloth and tied it with the supple twigs of the blackberry; I have been fed on oats' brew; moreover my mother often made me swear to her that I should never in my life make way for anybody.'

Hearing this, Marko threw his spear, aiming at Mussa's chest, but the Albanian received it on his mace and threw it behind him. It was his turn to throw his lance at Marko, but the Serb was as quick as his enemy. He, too, put his mace forward and broke the lance.

Both sabres were drawn out quick as lightning now, and the two foes charged at each other: Kralyevich Marko swung his sabre but Mussa put out his mace and shivered the sabre to pieces. When Mussa waved with his sabre, Marko met it with his mace and knocked it out of his enemy's hand. They fought with their maces now, but they, too, were soon broken. Dropping them on the green grass, the warriors dismounted and started wrestling in the little clearing by the roadside. Brave, fierce warriors both of them, they fought until noon-time without either proving to be the better of the other.

Raging with anger and fury, they continued fighting until Mussa shouted: 'Strike me hard, Marko, or I shall strike you to put an end to all this!'

Marko tried, but all in vain; Mussa finally succeeded in hitting him hard and throwing him on the green grass. He sat on his chest and was about to kill him, but Marko cried:

'Where are you now, Vila, my own sworn sister? Where are you today? May you be nowhere from now on! Why did you lie to me, swearing that you would be at my side if I ever should need your help?'

Vila's voice was heard from the clouds above them: 'Why, my brother, Kralyevich Marko! Did I not tell you so often never to fight on a Sunday? Moreover, it would be a shame for the two of us to attack one foe; but where are your secret snakes?'

Mussa looked up to the clouds, hoping to see the Vila. Marko, meanwhile, drew a knife out of his belt and gored Mussa from his throat down to the waist. The dead Albanian lay so heavily on Marko in the grass that the Serb could hardly breathe. After a while, however, he freed himself and rose, looking down at his enemy and marvelling at his strange body: there were three sets of ribs in his chest, and three hearts beneath them: one of them was weary, the other was prancing madly, whilst on the third a poisonous snake lay asleep. The beast woke with a start and spoke to Marko: 'You should thank God, Kralyevich Marko, that I did not awake while Mussa was still alive— had I not been asleep, you would have perished instead of him today!'

As he saw this, Marko wept bitterly, saying to himself: 'Woe to me, unhappy that I am; I have slain a hero mightier than I!'

Thereupon he cut off Mussa's head, put it in Sharin's oat-bag and rode back to Constantinople. When he was ushered into the big hall, he threw the head before the Sultan, who leapt up, terribly frightened.

'Fear nothing, my lord Sultan!' rumbled Marko. 'How would you face him alive when you so shake at the mere sight of his severed head?'

The Sultan gave him three packhorses loaded with treasure. Marko rode back to his city of Prilep, and Mussa stayed in his mountain gorge, never to disturb travellers or the Sultan again.

KRALYEVICH MARKO'S DEATH

 ARLY of a Sunday morning Kralyevich Marko was riding up a mountain, not far from the seaside. Suddenly the horse began stumbling under its rider, and Marko asked him, greatly worried: 'What is it, Sharats, my brave steed? It is now a hundred and sixty years that we have been companions, for better for worse, and you never stumbled before! Here you are now stumbling, and moreover shedding bitter tears. God grant I may be wrong, but I

fear this portends no good! One of us two is going to lose his head today—you or I, Sharats.'

Hardly had Marko uttered those words when a Vila cried from the mountain top, calling to Kralyevich Marko:

'Sworn brother, Kralyevich Marko, do you want to know why your horse stumbles beneath you today? Hear me now—he is mourning you, his master, for the two of you are going to part very soon, Marko.'

'O white Vila, may your white throat burn with pain! How can you speak like that? How could I part with Sharats when we have seen so many places and towns together, when we have been through this country from east to west, and I know that there is no better horse than Sharats and no better champion to ride him than I! I do not intend to part with my Sharats as long as I carry my head on my shoulders, Vila!'

'Sworn brother, O Kralyevich Marko, nobody will take Sharats by force from you, and you cannot perish by any warrior's hand, by his sharp sabre, heavy mace, or deadly lance. There is no man on this earth you ought to fear, but God who has decreed you to die. If you do not believe my words, look round when you climb up to the mountain top; you will see two slender spruce-trees, taller and more beautiful than any other tree in the woods; between them there is a deep well. Dismount your Sharats there, tether him to one of the spruce-trees, and bend over the well: you will see your face reflected in the clear water, and you will then learn your hour of death.'

Marko obeyed Vila, though with a heavy heart, and did as she had bidden him. Seeing the slender, tall spruce-trees, he dismounted from his brave steed and tethered him to one of them. He bowed over the well; as soon as he saw his face reflected in the calm water, he knew that his hour of death was very near. He wept bitterly, saying:

'O how false you are, world, my beautiful flower! Beautiful you have been but I have trodden over you such a brief time; woe is me! Such a brief spell, just three hundred years! And the hour of parting with you has already come, my hour of changing this world for another.'

Thereupon he drew out his sabre and cut off his brave Sharats's head so that Sharats should never be taken and used by the Turks, or be degraded by carrying water or any other burden. Marko buried him in a grave—deeper than the one he had dug before for his own brother, Andria. Heaving a deep sigh, he broke his sabre into four so that no Turk should be able to boast of possessing it, should he, by any chance, find it on the mountain. He did this also lest the Christians might curse him for leaving his glorious sabre to the heathen, who would use it against them. Then Marko took his lance and broke it into seven pieces of wood, which he threw high up among the branches. As for the six-knobbed mace, Marko hurled it mightily towards the deep-blue sea, saying:

'When my mace comes up to the surface of the sea, may a warrior of my stature and strength come into this world again!'

Having thus disposed of his weapons, Marko took a piece of paper, a pen, and a small golden inkpot which he always carried in his belt, and wrote as follows:

'Let him who should come up this mountain and find Marko lying by the well between the two spruce-trees know that Marko is dead. Marko has three purses of treasure with him. What treasure? Golden ducats, all of it! Let him who finds me take one purse for himself and may he be blessed for burying me; let him give the second purse to the churches that they may be repaired and adorned with new icons and ornaments; as for the third, let it be given to the crippled and the blind, so that they may walk through this world, singing their songs and speaking of Marko in them.'

Marko took the letter and threw it high up into the branches, and the paper stuck to one of them, easily visible from the road. Kralyevich Marko threw the golden inkpot into the well, took off his green surcoat, spread it on the grass under the spruce-tree, crossed himself and sat down, drawing his fur-lined helmet lower on his brow, and then stretched himself down, never to rise again.

Marko lay dead by the well for a whole week. Those going up or down the road saw him lying there and, believing him to be asleep, walked far around so as not to rouse his anger by awaking him from his sleep. Marko was known to be very quarrelsome if suddenly startled.

Finally, one day the abbot of the Serbian monastery of Hilendar, on Mount Athos, happened to be passing by with his deacon Isaiya. The old man saw Marko, and motioned his companion, whispering: 'Hush, my son, walk softly hither, for fear of rousing him. Marko is always angry when he first wakes up: he might easily behead us both before we know where we are.'

Still the monk glanced sideways at the sleeping Marko, full of curiosity, and looking up, he noticed the letter flapping on the branch. His younger companion climbed up, brought it down, and handed it to him to read. The abbot now learned that Marko was dead and hurriedly dismounted to touch him but—alas!—the letter had told the truth.

The monk thought for some time where to bury Marko and, finally, made up his mind: he put the dead champion on his horse and covered him with the green surcoat. He then took Marko down to the sea and carried him, helped by his deacon, on board a ship. The dead warrior sailed down the Adriatic sea to Mount Athos, where he was carried in state into the white monastery of Hilendar. The abbot said the prayers for the rest of his soul, weeping over the dead hero. He then buried him in the middle of the church and put the flagstones carefully back exactly where they had been before, leaving no mark by which Kralyevich Marko's grave could be found later on. This he did in order to ensure the warrior a peaceful rest, undisturbed by his enemies who might wish to take revenge even upon his dead body.

SERBIAN KNIGHTS AND OUTLAWS

FTER the battle of Kossovo in 1389, when the Turks
conquered Serbia, some feudal lords, in parts of the
country which were on the outer borders of the
Kingdom, or still farther away—like Montenegro,
for instance—kept their independence for a longer
or shorter period of time.

Ivan Tsernoyevich, father of Maksim in the following ballad, ruled
over Montenegro toward the end of the fifteenth century. The rugged,

wild mountains and, much more, the courage of the Montenegrins kept the Turks away, but the threat of their sudden onslaught was always present in the Montenegrins' minds.

The brothers Yakshich lived in the north, where Tsar Lazar's son, Stevan, ruled until that part of Serbia was also defeated by the Turks. They were knights, the sons of a duke, and they often came to blows with the Turks.

The Turkish rule became, as time went by, almost unbearable, for many of their feudal lords behaved as sole and absolute masters, extorting from the Serbs enormous taxes which they often could not pay, and taking away small boys of seven years old and training them in Turkey to be soldiers, *yanicharis*, and to forget all about their own origin, religion, and language. Quite often they succeeded, but there were a few among those abducted who, in spite of achieving great success and becoming Pashas and Viziers (people of highest importance in the Ottoman Empire), remembered where they came from and tried to alleviate the hard life of the people from whom they had been torn away by force.

Young women and girls were taken into slavery; men were tortured and murdered in the most atrocious way. All that forced the Serbs to desert the towns and live far from the highways, in out-of-the-way villages, most often surrounded, and somewhat protected, by dense woods.

This state of affairs could not go on without vehement protest, but as there was nobody to whom the Serbs, abandoned by all Christendom to their cruel fate, could turn, and no ear which would listen to their true tales of woe, they took the matter into their own hands. Instead of meekly waiting at home to be abducted, massacred, or humiliated beyond measure, young men and old, too, fled to the woods and, like the English hero Robin Hood, became outlaws. They took revenge on the Turks, attacking their lords and the merchants' caravans, arming themselves with the weapons they acquired in these skirmishes, and dealt justice according to their own minds.

Old Novak, Little Radoyitsa, Vukosav, and many others were outlaws in the days of Turkish rule in Serbia.

George Petrovich (Karadjordje—that is Black George, as he was called) started the first uprising in 1804 and became the Serbian leader in the fight for freedom, which, eventually, was won by his successor, Milosh Obrenovich, in 1830.

MAKSIM TSERNOYEVICH'S WEDDING

HE lord of Montenegro, Ivan Tsernoyevich, sailed across the deep-blue sea to Venice with three loads of treasure on board his vessel, intending to ask the Duke of Venice to give his daughter in marriage to his only son and heir, Maksim.

The Duke gave Ivan a friendly welcome, but learning the purpose of the Montenegrin's visit, he could not give a favourable answer on the spot. Pride made him dally with it. Truth to tell, he probably did not, in his heart of hearts, consider the Montenegrins as his equals. But if it comes to pride, there is hardly anybody in the world who can boast of being as proud, courageous, and honourable as a Montenegrin. Ivan, as their ruler, was no exception to this; on the contrary, susceptible to the slightest offence, he sensed the true reason of the Duke's dallying and that only strengthened his determination to obtain what he had come for—the Duke's fair daughter for his son Maksim.

The talks about the marriage went on for three whole years, in the course of which Ivan was freely spending his treasure in Venice. At last, when he had wasted almost all of it, the Latins agreed to give him the maiden for whom he was asking and, accordingly, accepted the ring he gave her in sign of betrothal. The Montenegrins and the Latins agreed that the wedding was to be celebrated in a year's time, after Ivan had returned to his home in Zhabliyak, gathered in the harvest, and made wine from his vineyards; he was to collect and bring a company of a thousand men for the wedding.

When all was settled and agreed upon, time came for Ivan to return home; on the day he was to heave anchor, the Duke of Venice, with his two sons and a retinue of a hundred Latins, came to see him off. Elated at having achieved his aim, the wise Ivan spoke unwisely, turning to the Duke:

'My dear friend, Duke of Venice, wait for me and my thousand wedding guests—there will not be less than a thousand, but there might well be more. When you see us approaching, send a thousand of your men to meet us: you will see then that among all those men, a thousand of mine and a thousand of yours, Latins, there will not be a single youth as handsome as Maksim, my dear son and your son-in-law!'

The Duke of Venice, his two sons and their hundred men heard his words with pleasure, and the Duke, gratified, spread his arms and embraced Ivan heartily.

'Thank you for your speech, dear friend,' he said. 'Since I am to have a son-in-law whose good looks are not to be found in thousands, I promise to cherish him as the apple of my eye, to love him more than my own sons: I shall bestow lavish gifts on him; he shall have the best hawks and horses, the costliest helmets, the most magnificent clothes to wear; I want him to be proud of them and of his own beauty. But if your words should not live up to the truth you will fare badly, Ivan, I give you my word for it.'

They bade Ivan farewell, and he sailed home full of happy expectations. After many days he reached his own shores, mounted his fiery steed, and rode to his home. Approaching it, and seeing the castle of Zhabliyak with the high tower dazzling white in the blue sky, the buttresses and towers clear against the mountains, and the windows sparkling in the brilliant sunlight, he drew in his horse's reins and stopped for a moment to admire the view, his heart swelling with pride and happiness.

The only person who saw him from a high window was his own wife: recognizing him and his brave battle-horse under him, she rushed away from the window and summoned her servants:

'Hurry down into the field to welcome your master! Come, maids, sweep the courtyards clean! And where are you, my son Maksim? Run down to the gates to welcome your dear father, your father and my beloved master; I saw him riding his horse: he seems to be gay and happy, and I believe he must be bringing us good news about our future daughter-in-law.'

The servants rushed down and met their master. His wife greeted him, kissing his hand, and took off his glittering arms which she then carried to the upper floors of their palace. The servants took the horses and led them to the stables.

At last his young son Maksim appeared, carrying a silver stool in his hands. Ivan sat down on it to rest and stretched out his legs so that the servants might take off his boots, but his eyes could never leave Maksim's face. What unexpected misery that sight was for him!

During the three years that Ivan had spent in Venice, trying to obtain the Duke's daughter in marriage for his son, smallpox had come to Zhabliyak and plagued its people. Maksim had been its victim too: the illness had left its big ugly marks on his once-white face, and it had grown dark, coarse, and ungainly. Indeed, it would be difficult now to find an uglier man than Maksim, Ivan's son, among thousands of others.

Ivan remembered how he had praised his son's beauty to his friend, the Duke of Venice, saying that there was nobody as handsome as he. Alas, now he could not help seeing that his ugliness was without pair.

This pained and saddened Ivan so much that he sat there, his dark moustaches falling down on his breast and his face gloomy, inscrutable. He would not say a word to anybody, and kept his eyes glued to the floor.

Seeing how unhappy he was, his wife sat beside his knee, saying: 'I beseech you, my lord, tell me what has made you so unhappy all of a sudden? Did you not obtain the Duke's daughter for your son? Or did she not meet with your approval? Or perhaps you are sorry for the three loads of treasure you spent on your journey?'

Ivan answered her through clenched teeth. 'She is indeed to be our future daughter-in-law, and I liked the Latin maiden. In the whole world there is no other as beautiful as she: there is no other maiden who can boast of such an eye, such a face, and such a fine figure! Even those who saw the Vila in the mountain would have to admit that she is not to be compared with the Latin maid. I do not regret having spent the three loads of treasure: there is much more of it in my castle here, and that which is gone does not make any difference to my wealth. The only thing that pains me, my wife, are the words I said to the Duke as I parted with him: I boasted that there was no other youth as handsome as my Maksim, and look at him now—there is none as ugly as he! I dare not think of what is likely to happen when those over the sea set their eyes on him.'

Instead of offering some comfort for his trouble, his wife reproached him: 'O my lord, why did you go so far for a daughter-in-law when you could have chosen any maiden from your own country, from any of our fine towns and honourable families? What great pride made you sail across the sea and bring such unhappiness upon all of us now?'

Ivan flared up, greatly angered by her words: 'I do not want to hear a word more about that wedding! If anyone should dare to come and bring me his good wishes on that occasion, I shall punish him severely!'

Word spread around about Ivan's wish, and everybody, low and high alike, heard of it; the Serbian lords, Montenegrins, acted according to his wish and none of them came to offer him his congratulations.

Not only did nobody mention the maiden or the wedding in the course of the first year, but eight more summers went by without a hint about it either from Ivan or anybody else. Finally, the tenth year brought a letter from the Duke of Venice:

'My friend, Ivan Tsernoyevich, when you fence off a meadow in the fields, you ought either to cut grass in it yourself, or let somebody else do so, for rain and snow will otherwise ruin it; likewise, if you choose a beautiful maiden for your daughter-in-law and obtain her father's consent, you ought either to take her away, or, if you never intended to do so, you should not have asked her hand for your son in the first place. You will remember our agreement: you were to come with a thousand wedding guests in a year's time, after gathering in the harvest and making wine from your vineyards. Nine years have gone by and neither you nor any of your wedding-party have appeared in Venice. You would be wise to answer this letter at once and return my daughter her freedom, so that she may marry another man, worthy of her. As for you, you may go and look for somebody unworthy as you are yourself.'

Reading the Duke's letter, Ivan was deeply disturbed: he felt the need to pour out his misery and troubles to somebody. As there was nobody else near at hand, he turned to his wife, and said:

'Advise me what I should do now, my wife. Should I free our daughter-in-law-to-be from her betrothal bonds, or should I remain silent? What am I to do?'

His wife answered wisely: 'O my lord Ivan Tsernoyevich, who ever took, or ever will take, the advice of women—who have long hair and small wisdom? However, I must tell you what is on my mind: it is a great sin before the face of God, and a shame and disgrace before the face

115

of men, to stand in the way of any maiden's happiness. Do as I now advise you, my dear lord. What does it matter if our son's face has been marked by the ill-fated disease? If the Latins are your true friends, they will not say a word—everybody fears a misfortune which might also befall him. Still, if you fear their wrath, summon your friends and retainers for the wedding—you have great riches and can do so; your vaults are full of treasures, your barns are bursting with wheat and your cellars are full of three-year-old wine. Instead of one, take two thousand men with you; choose the best youths and horses and go to fetch the maiden. When the Latins see such a splendid and numerous wedding-party, they will not dare say anything against Maksim even if he were to be blind. Therefore, my lord, summon your friends and go to fetch the maiden!'

Her words cheered Ivan and he laughed aloud. Soon afterwards he wrote a letter, gave it to a Tatar and dispatched him to the Duke of Venice:

'My dear friend, Duke of Venice, I shall soon be on my way to you; if you should care to listen, you will hear thirty cannons booming to mark my departure from Montenegro. As soon as you hear that, send ships down the Adriatic to meet me and my wedding company.'

After that letter he wrote several others and sent them to his friends, lords of various parts of Montenegro, asking them to come with their friends and retainers to Zhabliyak, which was to be the point of departure for the wedding-party. He advised them to wear their best clothes and helmets in order to show the Latins, who, although very skilled silver- and gold-smiths, and deft at making elegant garments, could not boast of such fine, good-looking youths as the Montenegrins. One of the letters he sent to his young nephew, the Captain Yovan, asking him to join him for Maksim's wedding.

Receiving their ruler's summons, all the lords, and not only the lords but also the peasants, who deserted their fields, and the shepherds, leaving nine flocks of sheep to but one among them—all and sundry hurried to Zhabliyak to take part in the celebrations. The whole vast field was densely covered by men and fuming horses, tightly pressed one to the other; there were so many lances planted in the field that they looked like a forest, and the flags and standards looked like clouds in the wind. Tents were pitched in the fields and the lords lay down to rest for the night.

Next morning, long before sunrise, the young Captain Yovan rose up and walked out of his tent, accompanied only by two servants. His face was gloomy and worried, his moustaches hanging sadly down his face. He walked over the ramparts, looking at the cannons, but very often his gaze wandered off over the vast field, full of people, horses, tents, lances, and flags. The sight did not cheer him and Ivan Tserno-yevich, standing not far from him, noticed his downcast air and could not help resenting it. He came to him, saying:

'Good morrow to you, my nephew Yovan! Why did you rise so early? What is it that worries you so, my son? Will you not tell your uncle?'

'Indeed I am worried, and I should like to have a word with you, dear Uncle,' Yovan answered instantly, 'but I know that it will be of no avail—you will not heed my warning. If you acted as I believe you ought, this is what you would do now: you would open your store-rooms and cellars, you would give plenty of food and wine to all those people down on the field, and you would send swift messengers to tell them to return to their homes without delay. Do you not see that all the menfolk from our country have come to take part in the wedding, and that there is nobody left to defend us from the Turks, should they attack our lands, once we have sailed off to Venice! There have been weddings before, Uncle: young men and maidens have been married before, and there have been great feasts to celebrate those occasions. However, there has been nothing like this before: you are taking all our men far away across the sea where people are not of our religion and where they might also dislike us. They could easily encourage some small private grudges, and our men might begin fighting between themselves; at the same time the country would remain deserted, defenceless.

'Besides, I had a very bad dream last night. I slept in my tent, well covered by fur-lined clothes and well cared for by my servants, yet the moment I went to sleep this is what I saw: a dark, foreboding cloud sailing across the sky towards your proud castle of Zhabliyak. Then, all of a sudden, Zhabliyak was struck by lightning and not a single stone of it was to be seen after the smoke had thinned out. One of the buttresses fell down on your Maksim, but fortunately he was able to extricate himself unharmed. I cannot tell you the rest of my dream, uncle, but if I am to believe in it, I know that I am going to die or be heavily wounded in your son's wedding celebrations. If anything should happen to me, there is more trouble coming; my five hundred fierce Montenegrins would stand up like one man for me: if I should moan, they would moan also, all of them; if I should perish, all the five hundred of them would perish too.

'I beg and beseech you now, dear uncle, disband the wedding-party and send them all to their homes. Give up the maiden to avoid misfortune!'

Being hot-tempered, stubborn, and proud, Ivan flared up: 'What nonsense you are talking, my nephew! A bad dream is just lies, nothing more. You may have turned in your sleep uncomfortably, or perhaps some gloomy thoughts had crossed your mind just before you fell asleep. Don't you know that I am sick of all this: everybody is laughing up his sleeve at me, lords and peasants alike, whispering about my son's betrothed, who after nine long years still lives in her parents' home. I will not give up the maiden or disband the wedding-party, and that is that!

'As you are to be the commander of all those men, and my son's closest cousin at the wedding, Yovan, I order you now to summon the gunners and have them fire the thirty cannons, in particular the two ancient, famous ones, which we won in glorious battles. Before that, however, send a warning to our men down in the field to take their horses away from the river Tsetina: the beasts might be frightened by the firing and might well jump into the rushing waters. Send word about the firing to all and sundry, so that there should be no panic once the cannons start booming.'

Yovan carried out all his uncle's orders dutifully. The cannons were fired, the men and horses taken good care of, and before long they all departed down towards the coast. They reached it after a while, and paused to rest before boarding the sailing ships which were waiting for them in the harbour. Soon they were all cheerful and merry: some of them riding their spirited horses up and down the field, some drinking good wine, and some singing the old, gay wedding songs. Ivan Tsernoyevich rode among his men, accompanied by two youths, his son Maksim and his good friend Milosh Obrenovich. After a while Ivan said to his assembled men:

'You all know, my brave young friends, where we are going and why. Unfortunately, the merciless illness has ruined my Maksim's face—and I had boasted of his good looks to the Latins! I hope you will all agree to this: in order to avoid bitter quarrels, fights, and possibly bloodshed with the Latins, let us tell them that Milosh, who is as handsome as my Maksim once was, is Maksim, my son; let us give him Maksim's princely helmet and sumptuous clothes and let him take the maiden from Venice. He will give her to Maksim as soon as we arrive back at our home coast.'

Nobody liked his idea very much, but they could not oppose him openly: Ivan was their chief lord and Maksim was also known to be rash. His wrath was feared, too. After a brief, uneasy pause Duke Milosh said:

'There is no need for you, Ivan, to ask anybody about that: give me your right hand—and I give you mine—and promise that I shall do your bidding, that is, bring the bride from Venice to your son Maksim. Moreover, I promise that there will be no trouble with the Latins on that account. However, I shall do it on one condition: that all the gifts I receive from them as bridegroom shall remain mine and not be disputed by anyone later on.'

Relieved that Milosh accepted his plan, Ivan Tsernoyevich laughed aloud at his last words:

'Why do you mention the gifts at all! Bring me my daughter-in-law to Zhabliyak, and you shall receive rich gifts from me too: to wit, two bootsful of golden ducats and my golden cup which holds two gallons of wine; I shall also present you with my grey mare who gives birth to fiery, bird-like foals, and, finally, you will have my favourite sabre which by itself would fetch thirty purses of gold. As for Maksim, he will stay here and await our return.'

No sooner said than done: Milosh donned Maksim's princely clothes and helmet and the wedding-party boarded the ships and sailed to Venice. Fair weather and favourable winds brought them to the foreign coast without any mishap. As they landed on another vast field, the city gates were opened and the Venetians came out in crowds to meet the wedding-guests and to see with their own eyes whether Ivan's words were true. It was easy to tell the bridegroom by his proud bearing, by his exceptionally good looks, and his costly clothes. The delighted Latins, the Duke's two sons, embraced him heartily and took him with Ivan to their father's palace; all the rest of the wedding-guests were also warmly welcomed and received by other Latins.

They stayed in Venice three or four days, to rest their horses and feast with their hosts. However, one morning the bugles sounded, heralds called, and the wedding-guests gathered to make the last preparations for their departure.

Soon they were all in the town square, but a surprise awaited them:

the city gates were shut and, according to an old Latin custom, four hangmen, two Latins and two Arabs, were standing by the gates; their arms were blood-covered up to their shoulders, and their sabres blood-stained up to the hilts. The wedding-guests were somewhat frightened by the sight. Seeing that two people were missing, they grew seriously worried. Milosh was not among them, and the Latin maiden, the Duke's daughter whom they had come to fetch, was also missing.

However, their fears were soon dispelled by the arrival of Milosh on his prancing bay horse. He greeted them all cheerfully and the Montenegrins shouted back, like one man: 'Good morning to you, our young Maksim!'

After a few seconds the Duke's two sons arrived too, bringing gifts to their brother-in-law which were to be presented to him in front of the assembled people. One of the Duke's sons led a jet-black Arab steed, with shoes, harness, and arm-plates all glistening with gold and silver; on his saddle the fair Duke's daughter was sitting and on the young Latin's arm a grey falcon was perched. He gave them all to Milosh, saying that his beauty was fit only for such splendid, royal gifts.

Milosh bowed from his horse and accepted the gifts graciously.

The second brother came forward now, carrying a precious golden sabre in his hands. He approached Milosh and hung the golden sabre on his belt, wishing that he might be happy and proud of it. The bride's father and mother arrived now. The Duke carried a helmet and a costly, plumed head-dress with such a bright, dazzling ruby set in it that it was almost impossible to look at the man who wore it on his head.

The Duke gave them both to Milosh, as to his dear son-in-law.

The Duchess came to him now, with a thin, fine shirt, all made of golden thread: the collar was made to look like a golden snake, its head coming out where the wearer's throat should have been. The snake's head was adorned by another large and bright ruby which would serve as a candle when the bride and bridegroom should depart to their nuptial chamber.

Milosh received both their gifts graciously as he had received the others before them.

Suddenly, a very old man with a white beard reaching down to his waist came forward, leaning on a staff; tears were trickling down his old, wrinkled face. He was the Duke's own brother who, having no children of his own, had brought up the Duke's daughter and was now grief-stricken at parting with her. He, too, had a gift for his son-in-law: he presented him with a most costly cloak, lined with the rarest and finest furs. 'No Tsar or King has ever worn such a fine cloak, my dear son-in-law,' he said. 'May you wear it in happiness and honour all your life long!'

When Milosh received all these princely gifts, the other guests were also presented with things befitting their position and rank, and all the horses' collars were adorned by the Latin maidens with embroidered handkerchiefs, as was the custom for weddings.

The wedding-party with the bride in their midst boarded the ships and sailed merrily homeward. But when they reached their own coast, the troubles began without any warning.

Maksim was at the head of the big crowd awaiting the arrival of the wedding-train in the harbour. As soon as the Montenegrins landed, Maksim hurried to the jet-black Arab steed and mounted it, wishing to ride up to Zhabliyak and tell his mother the good news about her daughter-in-law's safe arrival. At this, Milosh rode on his bay up to the bride and put his arm round her. She lifted the heavy golden veils off her eyes, and seeing him, her bridegroom as she thought, so near her, she put out both her hands to him. Several men who were near them pretended not to have seen anything, but Ivan noticed her happy look and cried:

'Hands off, daughter-in-law! Hands off! Cover your eyes, for shame! Do not look at that man—Milosh is a stranger to you. Look over there at the youth on the black Arab horse, with the golden armour—his face has been marked by smallpox—but *that* is Maksim, your bridegroom.'

He then explained why he had chosen Milosh to act as his son in Venice, adding that he had agreed that Milosh might keep all the gifts he was given there.

The Latin maiden, Roksanda, stopped her horse dead in its tracks and turned to Ivan, saying boldly:

'My dear father-in-law, why in Heaven's name did you have to do such a wrong to Maksim? You lost his happiness that way! What does it matter if smallpox has ruined his good looks? Anyone wise and reasonable would have understood that, for it is something which might befall anyone. If his face is pock-marked, his eyes are unharmed and his heart is the same as it was before his illness. If, on the other hand, you had feared that Maksim might look too young to my parents, why, I have been waiting nine years for him, and I would have waited nine more, honourably and patiently. But I cannot have a strange man keep the gifts which by right ought to belong to my husband. Take them all from him and give them to Maksim, or I will not move from here—even if you strike both my eyes out!'

Ivan was troubled and worried. How could he break the promise he had given Milosh? He did not wish to do so; on the other hand, there was the stubborn Latin maiden who also would cause trouble if he refused her request. At last he summoned his brothers and councillors and asked their advice. None of them felt inclined to encourage him to take the gifts from Milosh: they had all agreed before sailing away for the bride that those should not be disputed afterwards.

However, Milosh heard about the trouble and rode on his bay to Ivan: 'Is that the faith you gave me? Is that how you keep your word? Did we not agree I was to keep the gifts from Venice?' he asked, without dismounting. 'But,' he went on, 'I will not quarrel about that. I shall give you back the maiden and the Arab horse, although, if there was any justice, they should both be mine: the maiden was given to *me* by her father and her two brothers. But I shall keep my promise and shall give you all the gold and silver that is on the horse, as well as the grey falcon and the golden sabre. Indeed I am giving you all but three things: I shall not give you the plumed head-dress off my head, the fur-lined cloak off my shoulders, or the golden shirt. These I wish to take home to show to my brothers and to keep for myself. I give you my word: I *will* not part with those three things.'

All the men assembled around Ivan exclaimed: 'Thank you for your fair speech, Duke Milosh! Thank you for showing so much understanding and for agreeing so honourably!'

They were all pleased, believing the dispute settled, but the bride was not appeased. Her eyes shining and her face aglow with anger, she shouted across the field, calling Maksim by name, and Ivan rushed to her side and begged her:

'Daughter, do not call Maksim now; he is very hot-tempered. If he is not pleased with our agreement concerning the gifts he might pick some quarrel, and the wedding-feast might then become a bitter struggle. My vaults are full of treasure—I shall give all of it to you for your own use, only do not call Maksim now, daughter, I beseech you!'

The Latin maiden called again, not heeding Ivan's words. As Maksim did not hear her, she called out his name a third time. Only then did he turn round and ride back to her.

'Oh, Maksim, you are your mother's only son but it would be better for her to lose you too, if you are not the man you ought to be! May they make a stretcher from lances to carry you dead from here, and may they cover your tomb with your shield if you do not do as I now bid you! Shame on you all! Why did you let Milosh keep all those precious gifts? But I do not regret any of it—may the waters carry them away!—except the golden shirt. I have been weaving and embroidering it with my three friends for three whole years, wasting my eyesight on it, hoping that my beloved would wear it in my presence, and you are giving it away to a stranger! I cannot put up with it, Maksim! If you are a man, take the shirt from Milosh. If you will not do so, I shall not take a single step forward!

'I shall return to the coast, and with the blood from my own face I shall write a letter to my father, the Duke of Venice, and send it by a grey falcon. "Come to Zhabliyak," I shall tell him; "bring all your Latin lords and soldiers and come to ransack Zhabliyak." That is how the shame you brought on me is going to be repaid to you!'

Blood rushed to Maksim's head at her words: he bent low over his horse, whipped its flanks furiously, and rode off like a stormy wind.

Milosh, standing at some distance with the other Montenegrins, laughed aloud, asking: 'What came over our young Maksim to rush off at that speed?'

Hardly had he uttered those words when a lance, hurled by Maksim's hand, caught him between the eyes, just beneath the plumed head-dress, and killed him. Milosh fell off his horse and lay on the green grass, while his helmet rolled down the slope.

Still beside himself with wrath, Maksim rushed to him, cut off his head, threw it into his horse's oat-bag, took the maiden from Yovan his cousin, and rode off at full speed to his mother in Zhabliyak.

The death of such a fine and beloved young man as Milosh made all his friends' blood boil, and before anybody could say a word, rifles were fired, arms clattered, and men fought bitterly against one another.

The whole field was suddenly overcast by a dense cloud of gun-powder and leaden smoke; it was so dark, all over the field, that guns were no use any more. Swords were drawn out, and blood was flowing knee-deep all over the field. Many a mother lost her son there, many a sister her brother, and many a wife was left widowed there.

Walking in darkness over the bloodsodden field, Ivan prayed:

I   123

'O God, send a wind from the mountain to blow away this accursed fog, so that I may see who has fallen and who is still alive.'

God heard his prayer and very soon a wind cleared the air over the field. Ivan looked up and down, but wherever he turned his eyes, the sight was equally dismal: dead warriors and horses lay thickly on the grass, their lances and arms broken. Some of them, still alive though badly wounded, were moaning painfully. Ivan walked among them, turning the dead and wounded youths, looking for his son Maksim. He did not find him, but continuing with his search, he passed by his nephew Yovan without recognizing him.

'Wait, Uncle, what is it that makes you so haughty now? Are you so proud of your foreign daughter-in-law, of your wedding-suite, or of the wedding gifts that you will not look down on your unhappy nephew and inquire about his wounds?'

Ivan stopped and wept, seeing him. He lifted Yovan a little out of the blood where he was lying. 'Tell me, nephew, are your wounds likely to be healed? Shall I take you up to Zhabliyak and call physicians from the coastland to cure you?'

'Let me be, Uncle Ivan,' answered Yovan. 'Where are your eyes? May you see with them never more! These wounds cannot be healed: my left leg has been broken, my right arm cut off my shoulder, and my heart has been touched by a sabre.'

Seeing what a state the unfortunate Yovan was in, Ivan asked him: 'Whilst you are still able to speak, dear nephew, can you tell me what happened to Maksim—you were standing with his betrothed when he rushed to you—was he slain too? And what happened to the maiden?'

'Let me be, Uncle Ivan! Your Maksim is not dead. After killing Milosh, he took the maiden and rode with her up to his unhappy mother.' With these words Yovan breathed his last.

Ivan hastened up to Zhabliyak now and saw his son Maksim sitting in front of the city gates; he was writing a letter on his knees, with the Latin maiden to help him. His lance was stuck by the gates and the black Arab horse was tethered to it. Maksim, urged by his betrothed and desperate and out of his wits on account of the unexpected, tragic end of his wedding, was writing to his father-in-law:

'O my father, Duke of Venice, collect your men and arms, collect them and come to ransack my white city of Zhabliyak; take away your dear daughter, who has come and will go away as a maiden, not as my wife; I am sick of my lordship, sick of my kingdom, sick of this life! I wish to depart to other lands, to the Sultan of Constantinople, and when I arrive, I shall embrace the Moslem religion. I cannot continue to live as of old—I must change completely and become somebody else!'

Rumour about Maksim's decision spread quickly all over the country. Yovan, the brother of Milosh, heard of it too and quickly made up his mind what he would do. Taking leave of all his friends and relatives, he said: 'I shall also go to Constantinople and become a Moslem, but I shall do it in order to watch over your safety: if Maksim, in his madness, decides to lead an army and attack you and our country, I shall raise another army and attack him. Farewell, and God be with you!'

And that is how it turned out afterwards: both Maksim and Yovan were received by the Sultan; they both became Moslems and, very soon, high dignitaries at the Turkish court. After nine years, they both were named Viziers and were given lands to rule over and live by: Yovan, now Mahmut beg Obrenbegovich, was given good, fertile lands with all sorts of fine crops, whereas Maksim, who had become Skender-beg Ivanbegovich, was given the barren, rocky country of Skadar on the river Boyana. Nothing but buffaloes and frogs could live there, and the only crop he could gather was salt.

But the bitter fights which started in Montenegro on Maksim's wedding day have never stopped, and blood has been shed there almost up to the present day.

THE SICK DOYTCHIN

OYTCHIN, Duke of Salonika, fell ill one day; he was on his sick-bed for nine whole years without ever recovering. Many thought him dead, as they never saw him outside his home. The rumour of his death reached Hussein the Arab, and glad he was of the news! Now there was no one to thwart his wishes, he thought, and he rode straight on to Salonika. He stopped in a field beneath the city and sent a messenger, asking the champion of the city to come out and fight a battle with him.

Alas, in the whole town there was nobody to accept his challenge—nobody except Doytchin who lay on his sick-bed, unaware of the Arab's challenge. There were two other warriors, though, but one of them had a bad wound on his hand and therefore was not fit for the battle, whereas the other was still a boy—much too young. Although he was willing to accept the challenge, his old mother would not hear of it.

'The Arab is a cunning man and he will certainly win the battle by dishonest tricks. What am I to do then, lonely and old as I am?' she wailed, and the youth had to stay with her.

Seeing that there was nobody to face him on the battlefield, the Arab announced that the town had to pay special duty to him: each home was to give him a fat ram, a big basket full of white bread, a sheepskin of red wine, a beaker of hot brandy, twelve golden ducats, and—worst of all—a young maiden or a new bride who had just been brought to her bridegroom's hearth.

Sad and despondent, the townspeople obeyed the Arab's order, and each home gave him his due until the turn came to Duke Doytchin's home. His faithful wife and Yelitsa, his beloved young sister, collected all the Arab demanded, but there was nobody to take their offering to the tyrant; even if they could have persuaded one of their friends to carry the things to the tyrant, they knew that he would not accept them unless the maiden Yelitsa were included into the bargain.

Worried and unhappy, the two women busied themselves in the house until Yelitsa sat down in despair beside the sick-bed of her brother, weeping. The tears streamed down her cheeks and fell on her brother's face. Roused from his slumber, Doytchin murmured to himself: 'O my mansion—may you be swallowed by flames!—how is it that your roof has become rotten so soon? Why do you let rain leak through and disturb me so that I cannot even die in peace!'

'O my brother, sick Doytchin, these are no raindrops coming through your roof; these are your sister Yelitsa's tears, O brother!' said the maiden, sobbing.

'What is it, in God's name, sister? Are you short of white bread or red wine, sister? Have you run short of gold or fine white linen? Have you no more thread for embroidery—or, perhaps, is there nothing more to embroider?'

'O my brother, sick Doytchin, there is plenty of white bread and red wine in your home, plenty of gold and white linen, and I have all I need for my embroidery; something else made me weep over you. The Arab Hussein has come to the field beneath our town and we all, each household, have to give him what he demands. Each family has complied with his wish and given him what he wanted. It is our turn today. Everything is ready except—except that I cannot force myself to go to him and be kissed or to kiss the Arab whilst you are still alive, O my dear poor brother!'

'May wild flames turn you into white ashes, city of Salonika, when there is no brave champion in you to fight the Arab and let me die in peace!' cried Doytchin. He turned over in his bed and called his wife.

'Andjeliya, my faithful wife, is my bay steed still alive?'

'He is, my beloved lord Doytchin, he is alive and in good health, for I have always taken good care of him.'

'Good then, Andjeliya, my faithful wife. Take my bay steed to the smith Petar, to my sworn brother. Ask him to have my bay shod, and I shall pay him later on. I will go to meet the Arab on the battlefield even if I never come back to you.'

His wife took the horse out of the stables and led him to the smithy.

'What is it, sister-in-law, my sweet Andjeliya? Has my sworn brother died, since you seem to be taking the horse to be sold now?' asked the smith.

'He has not died, Petar; he sends you his greetings and asks you to shoe his horse, for he is going to fight the Arab. He will pay you when he comes back.'

'I do not shoe any horse by tally,' said the smith. 'But this I will do for you if you let me kiss your big dark eyes until your Doytchin comes back from the battlefield and pays me for the new horseshoes.'

Andjeliya flared up with fury and took the bay back, unshod, to his master.

'Has my sworn brother shod my bay steed?' Doytchin asked.

'He has not, may God's wrath smother him! He will not shoe your horse unless I let him kiss my dark eyes until you return from the battlefield, and that I cannot do, Doytchin, my lord!' she said, her voice still trembling with anger.

'Saddle my horse for me, my faithful wife, and bring out my battling lance,' was all Doytchin said in answer.

'And you, Yelitsa,' turning to his sister, 'you bring a piece of white linen and wrap me tightly from loins up to the ribs so that my bones shall hold together.'

Both women did his bidding hurriedly. When the horse was saddled, and the lance brought out from the armoury, and the poor sick knight wrapped in white linen, the women belted him and hung his splendid sabre on his belt and put him on to his saddle. His horse recognized him and started prancing gaily beneath him.

As Doytchin rode down the street, stones flew right and left from under his horse's old shoes and the merchants all looked at them, wondering:

'Thank God the Almighty for this! No better knight than this has ridden through our white town of Salonika since our Duke Doytchin died, and we never saw a better horse than this bay!'

Doytchin rode down to the field, and lo! The Arab recognized him and jumped up from fear, crying:

'O Doytchin, may God's hand strike you dead! So you are still alive? Come, then, sit down with me and let us drink this red wine like good friends. We had best make a truce, and I shall renounce the due this town had to pay me up to now.'

128

'Come and meet me in the battlefield, you black Arab! It is easy to drink red wine and kiss our maidens without fighting!'

'Be by God my sworn brother, Duke Doytchin; let us forget our quarrel, let bygones be bygones! Dismount your horse, come to drink wine with me, and I shall leave your city of Salonika and your young maidens in peace. I also promise never to return here, my lord!' the Arab pleaded.

Doytchin pressed forward, riding straight up to the Arab's tent: he turned it over with his lance and saw a strange sight. There were thirty Christian maidens inside, and the black Arab was seated among them.

Realizing that Doytchin would never relinquish the fight, the Arab jumped on to his black horse's back, took up his lance and rode out on to the battlefield. The horses grew angry, snorting at each other. Doytchin shouted now:

'You have the first throw, you villainous Arab, so that you shall have no reason to complain later on!'

The Arab hurled his lance, but Doytchin's bay was used to battles: he knelt down in the green grass and the lance flew over the head of his rider and stuck in the ground, far behind them; half of it stayed in the earth, and the upper half was broken and fell off.

The Arab turned back and tried to escape; he was streaming down the field towards the city gate, but the gate was firmly shut. Doytchin's lance nailed him to the door, and his sabre cut off his head. Doytchin took the Arab's eyes and wrapped them inside a silken handkerchief, letting his head roll in the green grass, and rode back into the town.

He stopped in front of his sworn brother's forge and called to him: 'Come out, Petar my sworn brother, come out and let me pay you for shoeing my bay and waiting for the money till now!'

'I have not shod him, Doytchin, my sworn brother; I just joked and your Andjeliya, quick tempered and rash as she is, flared up and took away your horse unshod,' the smith called back from the forge.

'Come out, I want to pay you,' Doytchin shouted again.

The smith came out, though reluctantly; Doytchin swung his sabre and cut off his head too. He took the smith's eyes, wrapped them into another handkerchief and, throwing the head into the town square, rode back to his mansion.

He took the handkerchief with the Arab's eyes first and threw it in front of his sister:

'There, sister, there are the Arab's eyes—know now that you will not have to kiss them as long as I live.'

The other pair he threw at his wife's feet: 'There, Andjeliya, there are the smith's eyes! Be assured that you will not have to kiss them as long as I live!'

Saying this, Doytchin lay down and died.

THE BROTHERS YAKSHICH
DIVIDE THEIR HEIRLOOM

THE Moon was scolding the Morning Star: 'Where have you been, what have you been doing, where have you been lingering for three whole days, shining Star?'

The Morning Star answered the Moon: 'I have been lingering over the town of Beograd, looking at something very strange indeed. The two brothers Yakshich, Dmitar and Bogdan, were dividing their heirloom. They divided their lands in a friendly way; Dmitar took the part in the north and north-east, down to the Danube, and Bogdan took the lands around the river Sava and in Serbia, down to the town of Uzhitse. They agreed easily over the city of Beograd too: Dmitar took the lower part with the tower on the Danube, called Neboysha, while Bogdan took the upper part with the church Ruzhitsa. When all the big questions were settled, the brothers quarrelled over a trifle—a trifle indeed, for they argued over a black stallion and a falcon.

'Dmitar maintained that he was entitled to both of them, being the elder of the two, but Bogdan would not hear of it.

'The next day Dmitar rose early in the morning, mounted the black stallion, put his falcon on his wrist and, before riding into the woods to hunt, called his wife, Andjeliya, and said to her:

' "Andjeliya, my faithful wife, take some poison and be sure that my brother Bogdan swallows it! If you do not obey this my wish, do not await my return here!"

'Thereupon he galloped away, and Andjeliya sat down, alone and sad, thinking of his words and saying to herself: "What am I to do, poor, miserable woman that I am! To poison my brother-in-law would be a great sin in the face of God, and a great shame in the face of men. Everybody, great and small alike, would cry out pointing at me: 'Look at that wretched woman who poisoned her brother-in-law!' On the other hand, if I do not carry out the wish of my husband I dare not wait for him here, for he might behead me in his wrath or do something else rash and irreparable."

'Andjeliya thought for a long time about her plight and finally something occurred to her. She leaped to her feet swiftly and went down into the cellar, took a cup wrought of pure gold, poured red wine into it and carried it up into her brother-in-law's chamber. She walked straight to Bogdan, kissed his hand and bowed low in front of him.

' "Take this cup, my dear brother, take the cup and drink this wine; may they both serve your honour, but I beg you, give me the black stallion and the falcon in return."

'Bogdan's heart softened at her sweet request and he granted her the gift she asked.

'Dmitar, meanwhile, was hunting in the woods. He had been hunting all day without any success. Towards evening he happened to pass by a clear green lake in the midst of the wood. How glad he was to see a gold-winged drake swimming in the water! He let the falcon off his wrist and the bird pounced on the drake, but the gold-winged one was the stronger of the two: he caught the hawk and broke his right wing.

'Dmitar cast off his clothes instantly, dived into the calm waters of the lake, and swam towards his wounded falcon. Reaching the bird, he put him on his own shoulder and carried him back to the shore.

' "How are you, my grey falcon, how are you without your right wing, my brave bird?" Dmitar asked him anxiously when they were on dry land again.

' "Without my right wing, my master, I feel as one brother without another."

'Only then did Dmitar remember what his wife was going to do that day. He jumped on to the black stallion's back and rode as fast as the brave horse could carry him back to Beograd, praying to find his brother still alive. He soon reached a bridge and drove the horse over it, but the horse's forelegs fell through the rickety planks and he could not move. Dmitar left a servant, ordering him to help the horse to escape from the broken planks, while he himself, unwilling to waste one precious moment, dismounted and continued his way on foot. Before long he reached Beograd and ran to his wife.

' "Andjeliya, my faithful wife, have you poisoned my brother?" he asked, hardly daring to hope against hope.

'Andjeliya looked at him and smiled: "No, my lord, I have not poisoned your brother, but have made up your quarrel for you."

'The two brothers were happier than ever in each other's company when I left them,' the Morning Star finished her story to the Moon, twinkling wearily after her long wake.

OLD NOVAK AND THE VILLAGE
ELDER, BOGOSSAV

OVAK and Bogossav were drinking wine by the cool river Bosnia, in the garden of a village elder. After much wine had been drunk, the villager spoke to Novak:

'My sworn brother, old Novak, will you truthfully tell me what made you become an outlaw? What misfortune drove you from your home out to the pathless woods, there to trudge many miles, to spend sleepless nights and to suffer as many hardships as they who take up the hard life of an outlaw? And all that in your old age, the least likely time for such things?'

'Since you ask me, I shall answer you truthfully, Bogossav. Great troubles forced me to it. Do you remember the time when Yerina, Despot Djurdje's wife, was having the city of Smederevo built? I had to work there for three whole years, carrying timber and stones for the building, using my own cart and oxen, my own food and clothes. For all that work I did not earn a farthing, not so much as to buy a new pair of shoes, and how many did I wear out during that time! But—I would have forgiven her that if there was not something worse to come afterwards.

'When the city was built, Yerina wished that all the doors and window-frames should be covered by a sheet of gold. In order to carry out her whim, she issued an order by which every household was to give her three hundred golden ducats! Those who had as much gold as that gave it to her and remained in their homes; but I, O brother, I was a poor man, without any gold or jewels to boast of. I had no choice and could do nothing but take my pick—the very one which I had used to help with the building of Smederevo, and escape from my home county towards the river of Drina. I crossed her cold green waters and reached the wild, mountainous Bosnia. Once there I went on, farther and farther from Serbia. I was approaching the huge mountain Romaniya when I came across a Turkish wedding-party. All the people of the wedding-party passed me by on the road without paying any attention to me, until the young bridegroom came to face me. He looked at me haughtily, took his three-stringed whip with sharp leaden weights at the end and hit me in the back—without any reason whatsoever. I said to him three times:

' "I beg you, young Turkish bridegroom, by your happiness, courage, and this merry occasion, let me go by peacefully—you see that I am only a poor old man who cannot mean any harm to you."

'But the Turk would not listen to my plea; he hit me even more cruelly than before. When the pain in my back grew more acute than I was willing to stand, I swung my pick and hit the Turk on horseback. He fell off his horse at once and I ran to him and dealt him some more blows, killing him then and there. I took his sabre and hung it on my own belt, drew three purses full of gold out of his pockets and put them inside my shirt. I left my pick by his head so that his people should have something to bury him with, leapt on to his bay horse and rode straight to Mount Romaniya.

'All the Turkish men who were with the wedding-party looked on from some distance and let me go without pursuing me. Whether they did not want or did not dare to do so, I still do not know.

'Anyhow, here I have been, living on Mount Romaniya for fourteen years now, and the dense mountain woods are more of a home to me than my own ever was! I know every path, every tree, every rock, and every spring in it better than I ever knew anything else. I keep watch over the woods here, waiting for the young Turks from Sarayevo to come my way and, when we come face to face, I take all their gold and silver, all their soft, costly clothes of silk and velvet which I and my companions wear in our green mansion. I can come quickly wherever I may be needed, can withdraw faster than anybody if necessary, but can also stand my ground in the most trying battle. I fear nobody but God Himself, brother!' said Novak, proud at having taken revenge for at least some of the wrongs the Turks were inflicting upon the Serbs.

IVO SENKOVICH AND AGA
OF RIBNIK

GA of Ribnik wrote a letter and sent it to Djurdje Senkovich. 'I have heard it said that you, Djurdje Senkovich, are a good champion, but *I* also enjoy a similar reputation among my own people. If you are willing to take up my challenge and come to fight with me, to see who is a better man of the two of us with his sabre, and who the braver on the battlefield, come to my white castle of Ribnik and let us test our strength and luck. If you do not accept my invitation, sit down at the loom and weave linen to make a shirt and some pants for me, so that I may then know that you are my faithful servant.'

Djurdje read the letter, tears streaming down his old, lined face. His son, Ivo, looked at him, astonished, and asked: 'Why are you crying, father? Letters have come to you before, and you have read them without shedding a single tear!'

'My dear child, Ivo, true, letters have come before too, but never like this one. Even if it had, for I may have forgotten it by now, your father was younger in those days and had no reason to fear anybody, or any letter for that matter. This comes from the Aga of Ribnik who challenges me to fight with him. I am very old now, my son; I can sit on horseback no longer, let alone chase a young Turk on a battlefield! As for weaving, I have not been brought up for it—I cannot weave linen for a Turk's shirt and pants, my son!'

'If you are old, my father, so old that you cannot go and fight with the Turk, here am I! God has given you a son to stand in your place, father. I shall go and be your champion,' said the son urgently.

The old man shook his head sadly: 'You may go to the battleground, my dear child, you may go, but if you do you will never come back to me. You are still almost a child, rash and without any experience— what, you are not yet sixteen! And the Aga of Ribnik is a proved, hardened fighter—there is not anyone to hold a candle to him for fighting prowess in all this part of the country. He is wrapped in furs of the wildest and rarest beasts, lynx and sable, my son; his horse is covered by thick bearskins: just to look at him you will be terrified, let alone when you hear the Turk's battle cry and his horse's fierce neighing! You will fall off your saddle and lose your head before the battle has really started. What will your father do then? Who will carry on our family and its name in the future, and who will provide for the poor old man I now am; who will bury him?'

'Why should I fear dead animals' skins when I do not fear live, wild wolves, father?' answered the youth with sparkling eyes. 'If the Turk can shout fiercely, so can I, father. Give me leave to go, bestow your blessing on me, father, and I shall go to meet the Turk on the battleground, for as long as you have your son Ivo, you will not weave linen shirts for any Turk, father!'

Djurdje had no choice now; he went to the stables and saddled his best steed for his young son. As he fixed the saddle, he pushed the brave horse's mane aside and kissed his neck, saying: 'O, my bay horse, my dear faithful friend! Have we not been to many battles together, have we not freed many Serbs from Turkish slavery, have we not brought back many a heathen head! But I have grown much too old, my bay horse, I am fit for battles no longer: I am sending you with an inexperienced youth now, with Ivo, my only son. Ivo is a foolish boy, my bay horse; keep watch over my child Ivo, I beseech you, my brave, dear bay horse!'

He then helped Ivo to dress, giving him his own best clothes; he hung his own sabre on Ivo's belt and looked him over, saying:

'O my Ivo, my dear child! Go now; may the hour of your departure be a happy one for us; may good luck be with you in the field! May God lead you safely; may He protect you from the foe's hands! May your right hand be firm and unfaltering; may your fine sabre be as sharp as a razor! May your eyes be as clear as a mountain lake in watching the Turk's movements!

'When you reach the white castle of Ribnik, my son, look sharply and speak sharply, my son; let your challenge to the Aga be sharp too. When the Turk comes out to the battlefield, do not confuse your bay by fumbling with the reins. I have trained him for battles, my son; he is used to battles and to fighting. He will screen you by his own body; he will dodge when necessary so that the Turk's sabre shall not touch you, my son!'

Receiving his father's advice and blessing, Ivo bowed low, kissed his father's hand and the ground he had trodden with his boots, turned to his mother, kissed her hand too, and said: 'Forgive me, dear parents!'

Thereupon he rode away singing, and his parents stayed behind, weeping.

After some time, the youth reached the field under the castle of Ribnik. He saw a white tent in the middle of the field; spears were stuck in front of it with good horses tethered to them.

Under the tent, Aga of Ribnik was drinking wine with two sons of a mighty Pasha. As they caught sight of the approaching horseman, the Pasha's sons said to their host: 'Here comes old Djurdje Senkovich, lord of Ribnik! You are going to lose your head and part company with us today, Aga.'

Aga of Ribnik narrowed his eyes as he looked at the rider, and then shook his head with a deprecatory smile. 'Fear not for me, dear brothers. That is not Djurdje Senkovich, but Ivo, his son. Unlucky was the hour his father sent him hither, for he will foolishly end his life today. But, on second thoughts, I may not kill him; he is a foolish, inexperienced youth and my victory over him would not mean very much. I shall capture him alive and ask a big ransom for him: I have heard it said that Djurdje is a very rich man, and I shall ask six loads of treasure for his only son.'

Hardly did he finish these words when Ivo arrived at the tent and greeted them: 'God be with you, Turks of Ribnik!'

'Good health to you, young warrior, Ivo Senkovich! What good brings you hither, Ivo? What good, why have you come to us?' asked the Turks.

Ivo asked, ignoring this queston: 'Who among you is Aga of Ribnik? Let him come out to fight with me. I have been molested by his letter —he challenged my father to fight with him. My father is a very old man now; I have therefore come here to stand in his stead!'

Aga of Ribnik raised one eyebrow and smiled, looking at him. 'Do not think of battles and suchlike devilish things! You have not seen a battle yet, let alone fought one, foolish youth! You had better come here and sit down with us to taste this sweet wine. It would be a pity to slay you, Ivo; you have hardly yet started living. Give yourself up; let us settle this without any wounds and without your losing your young head. As for me, I give you my word of honour that I mean no harm to you. Your father is very rich, they say; let him give some of his treasure to me and he may have his son with him again.'

'I have not come to give myself up, hear me, O Turk, Aga of Ribnik! I have come to fight with you, so come out into the green field, if you are no cowardly woman. I have no time to waste in idle talk!'

This infuriated the Aga. He uttered a wild cry, leapt to his feet and on to his black Arab steed in front of the tent.

'Spur on your prancing horse before charging up on me, young champion, Ivo Senkovich!' the Aga ordered him harshly.

'My horse is weary from the long journey, Aga, for I come from very far away. I will therefore toe the mark and wait for your onrush, Aga. I shall not move aside and shall wait for you without wavering.'

The Turk was very pleased that he should be the first to attack. His horse danced and, after a short while, the Turk held up his sharp lance and charged, roaring like a mountain dragon.

'Beware now, Ivo Senkovich; keep your eyes open to see that this is no trick now!'

He charged, his lance pointed at Ivo's heart. As he came quite near, the youth's horse knelt down on the green grass and the lance swished through the air over Ivo's head, without even touching his casque. Ivo swung his sabre quickly and cut off the lance up to Aga's hand which had been holding it.

Seeing what kind of champion he was confronted with, Aga turned round, riding fast towards the castle of Ribnik.

Ivo let out the reins of his bay steed and galloped, catching up with him very soon, although his horse was worn out. The bay reached the

K

black Arab, leaned his head on the Arab's croup, and bit off Aga's fringed belt.

'O, Allah, that I should die this way! If I were slain by a valiant champion, I would not mind it so much, but to be conquered by Ivo's brave horse!' the Turk muttered to himself.

Instead of drawing out his sabre and cutting off Aga's head, his youthful, inexperienced foe Ivo rode after him, wishing to catch him alive and lead him as his own prisoner to his father, as the best proof of his prowess. Meanwhile, the Turk remembered his rifle, raised it quickly and fired backwards over his shoulder. The bullet missed Ivo, but struck his brave bay between the eyes. The horse crumpled down on to the green grass and Ivo sprang up to his feet.

Aga of Ribnik turned his Arab stallion back, seeing that he had killed the bay horse. He said to Ivo:

'What are you thinking now, what hoping for, foolish youth? I have deprived you of your valiant horse. There is nothing left to you but to give yourself up, Ivo Senkovich! As a slave you may still nurse some hopes of life, but once in your tomb, there is no hope left for you, nor anybody else.'

'No, Turk, Aga of Ribnik, you will never have me alive! If you have deprived me of my valiant horse, I still have my weapons. Here is my father's sharp sabre which has seen many battles and cut off many Turkish heads. As God is merciful, I hope that it will sever yours too from your body today!' Ivo shouted back, fiercely.

The Turk uttered another of his frightful cries and drove his horse up to Ivo, but the youth was a valiant, though inexperienced warrior: he did not falter or move an inch from the spot where he was standing. He swung his sabre with all his strength and cut off the stallion's black head. The horse fell down with the Aga lying under him, helpless. Ivo Senkovich laughed, standing above him.

'What are you thinking now; for what are you hoping, Aga of Ribnik?' he asked.

The Turk spoke in a very different tone now, pleading: 'Be by God my sworn brother, Ivo; do not behead me today and I shall give you all you should care to name as a ransom for my life.'

'No, Turk, I prefer your head to all the Tsar's riches and treasures!' Saying this, Ivo beheaded him and threw his foe's head into an oat-bag. He now undressed Aga and donned his clothes himself.

Meanwhile, the two Pasha's sons who had been watching their

battle said: 'We will not let this foe of ours escape alive. Let us go after him to avenge our friend's death!'

They leapt into their saddles and galloped down the field after Ivo. Although without his mount now, Ivo ran faster than the wind and, with God's help, reached the mountain before the Turks could catch up with him. The rocks were very steep there, and Ivo, jumping from boulder to boulder, quickly disappeared behind the leafy trees. The Turks saw that they could not follow him on horseback; they dismounted and, having tethered their horses to a spruce-tree, ran on foot after him.

However inexperienced he may have been, Ivo was a clever youth: he lured his pursuers into one direction, and then, screened by the dense foliage, managed to steal back unnoticed. He untied the horses, mounted one of them and, leading the other by the bridle, rode up the mountain path.

'Thank you, you two Turks, worthy sons of the great Pasha, thank you for giving me your fine horses today,' Ivo shouted from the mountain heights.

The Turks heard him and rushed towards the path. At the last moment they held back, fearing Ivo now. They called to him, hidden by a clump of trees: 'Be a brother to us, in God's name, Ivo Senkovich, give us back our purebred horses and we shall pay you six hundred ducats for them!'

'Do not be fools, Pasha's sons! I prefer these two purebred horses to all the treasure there is in your castle of Ribnik. Go back now—I have no wish to pursue you on this mountain—go back to the black stallion and the brave bay horse, the better of whom the world has never seen!'

Saying this, Ivo went his way singing happily and the Turks remained on the mountain, weeping bitterly.

Ivo's mother was anxiously watching the road from a window. As she saw a horseman approaching her heart almost stopped beating. When the man drew nearer she sobbed desperately, for she did not recognize her own son in the Turkish clothes, mounted upon a strange horse. She ran down the steps, blinded by tears, and called to her husband:

'Woe to us, Djurdje, my dear lord! Unhappy was the hour you sent our Ivo to be your champion! Ivo fell on the battlefield—here is Aga of Ribnik coming to ransack our mansion and to enslave both of us so that we should serve him, a Turk, in our miserable old age!'

Old Djurdje could not stop tears from running down his ravaged face; yet he jumped to his feet after a moment, put his sword in his belt, ran out to the meadow and caught his old mare. He leapt on to the horse's unsaddled back, having no time for any preparations, and rode to meet the Turkish Aga.

He shouted at him, as soon as they came nearer, unable to recognize his son:

'Stop where you are, you scoundrel, Aga of Ribnik! It was easy to do away with a youth who was not yet sixteen, but come and try to slay me, old as I am, and you will see what a real battle is!'

'God be with you, my dear father Djurdje! I am not Aga of Ribnik; I am your own son Ivo.'

Disturbed by his great grief, his view obscured by tears which were still in his eyes, the old man neither heard nor saw who was talking to him. He charged at Ivo, firmly determined to behead him. What a strange plight young Ivo was now in—to be killed by his own, loving father! Realizing the peril threatening him, he turned his back and galloped away, but the desperate old man whipped his mare and rode after him. 'Stop, Aga, you will not escape me!' he shouted.

Before long he was near Ivo again. The youth saw that he was going to lose his head by his own father's hand. Only then did he remember the other head. He took it out of the oat-bag and flung it towards his father.

'God be with you, my dear father Djurdje, here is Aga of Ribnik's head!'

As it fell on the ground before him, Djurdje recognized it. He dismounted his mare, ran to Ivo, took his horse's reins and, helping him to dismount, embraced and kissed him with great joy.

'Thank you, Ivo, my dear child! Thank you for having fought my battle, for having won great honour on the battlefield for all of us, all the Serbs from this country. But why did you don the Turkish clothes? Your father nearly killed his own son; he nearly burdened his soul with a heavy, unforgivable sin!' the father said, looking at his son with new pride and happiness.

'How would our lords know that I had been fighting with Aga of Ribnik when they saw me? They would not believe it if I had nothing to show as a remembrance from that battle,' said the youth.

They now returned to Ivo's mother, whose happiness knew no bounds at seeing her young son, victorious and unharmed.

THE KIND PASHA AND MIHAT
THE SHEPHERD

ERALDS came in, one after the other, into the Pasha's
lordly mansion, all with the good news on their lips:
'Your men, illustrious Pasha, are bringing the outlaw Mihat the Shepherd, captured at last!'

After a while Mihat himself was ushered into the
Pasha's presence; the Pasha kindly offered him a seat
at his side.

'Tell me the truth, Mihat the Shepherd. Is it true what people say
about you—that you have a fine homestead in the town of Prizren, a
home consisting of seven houses in a paved courtyard, each house with

a golden lock in the door? Is it true that you have a huge black horse whose reins are like snakes, and whose mane resembles a deer's beard?

'Is it true that you have nine peacocks who stroll in your gardens followed by nine peahens; they say a wise otter leads them all and at the rear of the train walks a gold-winged duck. Among them there is a beautifully adorned marten who is, in fact, your faithful young wife. She is so white and pink, they say, and her skin is so delicate and transparent that you can see water or wine go down her throat when she drinks it! And yet you, young man, do not care for her, fair as she is, but go around kissing other maidens in Prizren, honouring some of them that way and putting others to shame.

'Is it true, moreover, that you have a green meadow where you cut grass and gather hay three times in the course of one single year?'

'All that you heard is true, Pasha, my dear master! Not a single lie among all those rumours. The nine peacocks are my nine dear brothers, and the peahens their faithful wives, my sisters-in-law; the wise otter is our mother and the gold-winged duck our sister,' said Mihat.

'Why then, Mihat the Shepherd, since you have all this, why did you become an outlaw? Why did you choose to live in the woods, to kiss Turkish maidens, and to kill my horsemen, when you could have lived peacefully in your own home, with your own people?' the Pasha asked him, puzzled.

'You will hear the truth, Pasha,' began Mihat. 'As for my kissing the Turkish maidens, this is how it happened. When the spring came and all the mountains became bright and sweet-scented with many roses, peonies, and all kinds of wild flowers, the Turkish maidens used to walk up into the woods, picking flowers and singing. They used to hang wreaths and bunches of flowers on my arms and then—even you, Pasha, would not be able to resist temptation, let alone I, foolish young man that I am!

'As for your other question—why I had to go to the woods and become an outlaw—you will have the answer now, honourable Pasha. My green meadow remained bare one summer—there was no grass on it and I had to provide food for my sheep. I drove them all down to the river Morava and grazed them in a meadow. I had exchanged, on the way, a thousand of them for enough hay to feed the others, but another thousand perished on the road. I was left with three hundred sheep and a hundred rams; soon afterwards three hundred lambs were born. It so happened that at that time a party of your three hundred horsemen passed me by on the road: they all went on except thirty of them who turned round their horses, came back to me, and took thirty lambs from my fold.

'When the time came for the lambs to be let to their mother's fold to suck, the thirty sheep who had no lambs started bleating desperately, looking at Mihat, their shepherd, and hoping that I would let their lambs come to them. The look in their eyes broke my heart, Pasha; I called my ten shepherds, ten brave men, and we all rushed on the road, made an assault on the thirty Turkish horsemen, and took back the thirty lambs which we then returned to their mothers.'

'O Mihat, foe of the Turks, remember this now: where some serious danger threatens somebody's goods and chattels as well as his own life, unless the goods can help the man to save his head, let the lightning strike them and let them perish with their owner and master. If on the other hand, the master does nothing when his goods and chattels are jeopardized, let such a man perish by his enemy's hand!'

Thereupon the Pasha gave Mihat a hundred ducats and a posse of his own men to escort him safely home. When they reached Mihat's homestead, the shepherd took his fine black horse out of his stables and sent it as his gift to the kind, righteous Pasha who, by those qualities, earned the name of Good Man Pasha.

OUTLAW VUKOSSAV'S WIFE

 YOUNG Turkish lord, Alil Boyitchich, went a-hunting into the mountain woods, accompanied by his soldiers, servants, and dogs. He hunted up and down the mountain for three days without catching anything at all. Towards noontime of the third day, however, his efforts were rewarded, but not by the game he had been expecting: he caught an outlaw who had left his gentle native country by the seaside to live in the green mountains. Alil Boyitchich, very pleased by his catch, boasted to his friends: 'I shall take this outlaw, this Vukossav, to the Sultan himself, and shall give the rascal to our mighty lord as a rare, precious gift.'

However, he changed his mind later on and, instead of giving him as a slave to the Turkish Sultan, he threw him into a deep, mouldy dungeon and let him lie and rot there for three whole years.

'O Turk, Alil Boyitchich, give me some white paper and a pen to write with, for I wish to send a letter to my mother and to my wife,' said the exhausted prisoner one day at the end of his third year.

The Turk gave him some paper and a pen. The outlaw sat down and wrote this letter on his knees:

'My dear old mother, do not nurse any more hopes for me, and you my faithful wife, do not wait for me—you are free to marry another man now!'

Receiving the letter, both his mother and sister wept bitterly, but his young wife burst out laughing. She went out of the house, walked down the main street, and stopped in front of a barber's shop.

'Be in God's name my sworn brother, barber Mihat,' she addressed the man. 'Shave my hair, leaving it long only on top, so that you can make a tress like those that the Turkish warriors wear on their heads.'

The barber did her bidding without asking unnecessary questions. The young woman covered her head with a kerchief, returned to her mansion, and put on splendid clothes: first a white cotton shirt, and over it another one with fine golden embroidery; she then put on trousers, buttoned down at the sides so as to fit the leg snugly; over them she donned a warrior's armour, belted her waist with a costly girdle into which she stuck two small, beautifully wrought guns, and between them two golden scimitars. She then put on her head a casque with trembling, rare feathers and walked out to the stables to saddle a horse for herself. She chose the best steed, put a silver saddle upon his back and covered him with a fine trapping reaching down to his knees, the fringe lightly touching his hoofs. Before mounting her horse, she covered his back with a bearskin and hung a row of pearls interspersed with jewels around his neck, so that they should shine and light her way, even at the darkest hour of midnight. Having made all her preparations, she lightly jumped into the saddle, picked up a heavy mace, and hurled it skywards to test her strength.

The mace rose high into the clear, blue sky and fell back into her white hands.

Coming out of her own courtyard, she rode down the main street again, touching her steed from time to time with a whip: the horse walked proudly, strongly; stones flew right and left from under his mighty hoofs, hitting the shopkeepers who stood gaping in their

147

doorways. The strange young horseman stopped by the barber's and spoke in a low voice, bending to him:

'Mihat, my dear sworn brother, had you not shaved my hair yourself, would you say, seeing me now, that I was a woman?'

'I swear, my sworn sister, had I not cut your long dark hair by my own hand, I would say you were a fine warrior, a distinguished knight of the Sultan,' said the barber.

Pleased with his answer, the young woman rode on towards the mansion of the Turk Alil, never stopping, never moving one inch from the middle of the road; all those who came her way had to move aside and let her pass, awed by her splendid appearance. Thus she entered proudly the Turk's own courtyard on horseback. Alil saw her from a window and ran out to receive her as befitted such a fine warrior. He took the horse's reins, wishing to hold them whilst his guest dismounted. He hoped he would thus pay him due respect. But the unknown warrior hit him in the back with his heavy mace, showing no appreciation of his hospitable ways.

'Go away, you scoundrel!' the young knight shouted angrily. 'Do you think you are the Sultan himself, since you dare keep in your prison those who rebel against him? I have been sent by our mighty lord, the Sultan, to take both you and the outlaw to him, for he is going to behead you together, self-willed rebels that you are!'

The frightened Turk bowed low and waited humbly for her to dismount. When she finally did so, he led the horse, walking with him up and down the courtyard so as to let the animal cool down gradually after his long ride. The young knight lit a long pipe and stood by, watching him haughtily. After a while the Turk thought he had walked the horse long enough and approached the knight again and again, glancing at him sideways and hoping that he would at last dismiss him. But the knight would not do so, not for a long time. At last, he spoke grimly:

'Take my horse to the stables now, and give him plenty of oats and hay. After that you are to prepare a good supper for me. I want you to bring to the table the best and rarest food there is: I want to have good, juicy mutton from the district of Skadar, unleavened round bread from the Field of Kossovo, red wine from the Bulgarian town of Vidin, and hot brandy from the Macedonian place of Demir Kapiya. I want to have all this for my supper, or your head will come off your shoulders this very evening!'

The terrified Turk ran out; he rushed throughout the town to find all that his unexpected visitor had ordered for his meal. After much trouble, he bribed and persuaded those who had the required food and drink to give it to him, but they would do this only in exchange for enormous sums of money. He collected it all and laid it out for the lordly youth's supper. To soothe his obvious wrath, the host Alil held the candles himself, lighting the room for his guest who ate slowly but with gusto, enjoying both the food and the candlelight. He did not dismiss his host until very late in the evening. Each of them repaired to his own room, the guest to sleep peacefully and contentedly, the host to be troubled by frightful nightmares.

Early next morning the lordly youth arose, dressed, and, fully armed, walked towards the dungeon. He made quick work of the jailer, beheading him before the man knew where he was. Then he pounded the door open with his mace and shouted:

'Come out, you Sultan's own prisoner! Come out, for I have been sent by our mighty Sultan to take you and Alil to him so that he may punish you as you deserve, self-willed rebels, both of you.'

The Serbian outlaw Vukossav was fed up with his miserable life in the dungeon, and he walked out without any delay, though he believed that it was to his own death that he was walking. The young Turkish knight looked at him with contempt and hit him two or three times with his mace; all the servants were gaping and trembling in their shoes. The youth turned to the mansion and shouted to the invisible Alil:

'Hey, you Turk Alil, give me a horse for this wicked outlaw and prepare yourself and your own steed quickly. We are to depart without any delay—the journey to the Sultan's city is ahead of us; it is long and I'm pressed for time, remember, you wretched dog!'

Alil ran to his armoury, picked up his best, most precious sabre, and then ran out into the stable where he chose the best horse. Before going to the young knight, he took a big purse and filled it with golden ducats from his treasury. Only then did he face the Sultan's emissary.

'Take all this, illustrious lord, Sultan's honourable knight—take these humble gifts as a ransom and leave me here in my mansion, I beseech you,' he mumbled dejectedly, bowing to the ground.

The youth accepted the costly gifts without as much as a word of thanks, sprang up into the saddle, ordered the outlaw to mount the other horse, and rode away down the green field. The two horsemen travelled for some time without exchanging a word, but the haughty Turkish lord finally turned to his prisoner when they reached a crossing: one of the roads led to Constantinople and the other to the gentle coastland.

'Look well at me, you wicked outlaw! Can you recognize some of the arms I am wearing now?'

'Indeed I can,' said Vukossav, looking grimly at his own guns and scimitars. 'I know who they used to belong to, but do not know how they came to be in your possession, Turkish knight.'

'That I shall tell you myself, wicked outlaw: your own wife brought the arms as a gift to me and I took both the arms and her who is to be my wedded wife.'

Vukossav grew paler than a sheaf of white paper and began trembling with pain, so much that the youth burst out laughing. It was a gay, tinkling, girlish laughter.

'Fear nothing, my dear lord, for I am your wife,' the young woman said, pushing the helmet off her brow. 'Forgive my hitting you with the mace, but I had to do it in order to avoid any suspicion in the Turks.'

They kissed heartily and turned their backs on the Constantinople road, taking the other one to the coastland. They rode on, gay and happy; and gay and happy will their mother be when she beholds them together again; and may you, who listen to me, be as gay and happy as they and their mother were on that day!

LITTLE RADOYITSA

LORIOUS God, O what a great wonder!
Is it thundering, or is the earth trembling?
Is the sea beating the marble rocks, or are Vilas
fighting on the mountain?
It is not thundering, nor is the earth trembling; the
sea is not beating the marble rocks and Vilas are not
fighting on the mountain.

Great guns are being fired in Zadar: Bechir Aga is rejoicing and
celebrating a conquest. He has captured the outlaw, Little Radoyitsa,
and has thrown him in the lowest dungeon.

There were twenty prisoners there before Radoyitsa came, and they
were all weeping and mourning their sad fate; only one among them
found it in his heart to sing and thus comfort them:

'Do not weep, O my dear brothers! God will send a hero to free us
from our slavery.'

When Radoyitsa was thrown among them, great despair seized
them and they all wept more bitterly than before, scolding him:

'May you live to be terribly tortured, Radoyitsa! We laid all our
hopes in you, believing that you would free us from this dungeon one
day, and here you are now, in the same plight as us! Who is going to
free us now?'

'Do not lose heart, my dear brothers, but heed my words and do as
I bid you. Tomorrow morning call Bechir Aga and tell him that Little

151

Radoyitsa has died during the night. He may bury me, and the rest is my own business,' said the outlaw, smiling.

As soon as the sun rose next morning, the twenty captives called as one: 'Accursed be you, you Turk, Bechir Aga! Why did you not hang Little Radoyitsa last evening? Why did you let him come among us here, for he died last night and his body is rotting among us. We shall all perish by this vile air!'

Aga's men opened the heavy, iron door and carried out the stiffened Radoyitsa. Bechir Aga glanced at him and waved his hand at the prisoners: 'Take him away and bury him,' he ordered.

His wife looked on suspiciously. 'He may not be dead, Aga my husband, he may just be pretending. Let someone kindle a fire on his breast: we shall then see whether he moves or not, the cunning scoundrel.'

The servants hurried to do their mistress's bidding. A bright fire was soon leaping from Radoyitsa's breast. Under that breast was the heart of a hero who stood the torture without wincing or making the slightest move.

Bechir Aga's wife never let him out of her sight. Yet she was not satisfied with the stiff immobility of the would-be corpse. When the fire died out she said to the servants:

'Go to our garden and fetch one of the snakes basking in the sun. You shall put it inside Radoyitsa's shirt; if he is alive, the cunning scoundrel, he will be frightened and will certainly give himself away by a cry or a shiver.'

They fetched a snake from the sunny side of the garden, brought it and put it on Radoyitsa's breast, but his brave heart withstood even that without flinching.

Yet that still did not convince the suspicious Turkish woman. 'I still do not believe he is dead,' she said, pondering. 'Oh, I know,' she exclaimed. 'Take ten iron nails and drive them under his fingernails. We shall see then whether the pain will force the cunning scoundrel to move or to wince.'

This the servants did: the nails were driven under Radoyitsa's fingernails but his brave heart withstood that too. He neither winced nor drew a breath, in spite of the pain. Bechir Aga's wife walked around his prostrate body and thought for a while before striking on a new way to test him.

'I still do not think he is dead,' she said. 'Call all the young pretty maidens from our mansion and bring particularly the fairest of them all, our daughter Haykuna. She is to lead the *kolo* around him. He must smile at her if he is alive.'

The girls gathered around Radoyitsa and Haykuna. The fairest of them all began the *kolo*, dancing and jumping lightly to and fro around him as she led the others. Oh, what a beauty that maiden was! Tall and fair, shining like a bright star among her companions! Her necklaces, rows of golden ducats and precious stones, were tinkling gaily in rhythm with her dancing steps, and her silken Turkish trousers rustled with every movement of her graceful young body.

Little Radoyitsa could not help slightly opening his left eye to catch a glimpse of her; as he did so, his right moustache curled up with a smile. Haykuna saw it and quickly took off her velvet bodice. She covered his face with it, hiding it from her dancing companions and all the other onlookers.

'O dear father, do not commit such a heavy sin as this! Your captive is certainly dead—let our men take him away and bury him,' she said to Bechir Aga, letting herself out of the reel.

'No, do not bury the scoundrel, for that would be much too good an end for him. Throw him into the deep blue sea instead; let the fish feed on his rebel's flesh,' hissed her mother, Bechir Aga's wife.

Bechir Aga went on the boat with his oarsmen and he himself threw Radoyitsa into the sea, far from the coast, far from any island or islet. But Radoyitsa was a good swimmer. As soon as the oarsmen had turned their backs on him, he swam ashore and climbed a hill nearby.

'O my strong white teeth, take out these nails from my smarting flesh!' he said aloud to himself, drew the nails out, and carefully put them inside his shirt.

He waited for nightfall and then lightly walked back to Bechir Aga's mansion, stopping in the dark shadows by a lighted window. Peering in, he saw Bechir Aga and his wife who had just sat down to their supper. The Aga heaved a sigh of relief and said, turning to his wife:

'O my dear faithful wife, it is nine years now since Radoyitsa went to the woods and became an outlaw, nine years since I could eat my supper in peace, or go to sleep without fearing him. Allah be praised that he should not be alive any longer. Thank Heavens that I have put an end to him and to my own anxiety! Only now can I safely hang my other twenty captives, and that I will do tomorrow, as soon as the day grows light, dear wife!'

153

Radoyitsa heard and saw all that was happening in the lighted room. Without thinking, he rushed in, caught the Aga and strangled him on the spot, and then turned to his staggered wife. Taking the nails out of his shirt, he made as if to drive one under her fingernail. Hardly had it touched her flesh when the Turkish woman breathed her last, from pain or terror—who could tell? Little Radoyitsa looked at her, saying: 'There, Bechir Aga's wife, you now know how much driving nails into your flesh can hurt!'

Radoyitsa ran out and found Haykuna. 'Haykuna, my own dear heart, go and find the keys of the dungeon, for I want to let the twenty captives out of their mouldy, sad abode.'

Haykuna found the keys quickly and the captives were let out of the dungeon.

'And now, Haykuna, my dear soul, go and find the keys from the Aga's treasury—the treasury he built up by plundering us Serbs and Croats. I want to take some of the treasure with me, for long is my journey and thirsty for wine I am, sweetheart.'

Haykuna gave him the keys and they descended to the vaults together. She opened a chest full of big silver coins and urged him to take as many as he wanted.

'No, Haykuna, my dear heart, what am I to do with these heavy silver plates? I own no horse to have shod with them. You had better open the other chest for me with the golden ducats.'

Haykuna obeyed him readily. Radoyitsa took all the ducats and divided them between himself and the twenty liberated captives, who then departed each to his own home.

As for Radoyitsa, he took Haykuna by the hand and led her over the river Drina to Serbia, on to a white church. Haykuna was christened there; changing her Turkish name for the Serbian, she became Andjeliya and that very day she was married to Radoyitsa, to whom she was a good and faithful wife all her life long.

IVAN OF SEMBERIYA

APTAIN Kulin, the Turkish Commander in Bosnia, raised a numerous host of Bosnian Turks and marched with them towards Serbia, to the rich lands around the rivers Sava and Drina. Wherever he passed, he threatened the Serbs:

'Beware, Serbs! When I come back I shall greatly reduce your numbers! You will have cause to remember Captain Kulin for a long time to come!'

Christian mothers, Serbian women, set a curse on him:

'May you go where you are going now, Captain Kulin, but may you never come back!'

Kulin passed through the proud country of Bosnia and reached the border between Bosnia and Serbia, the green river Drina. As soon as he crossed it, he ordered his soldiers to camp in the field and dispatched messengers to the Serbian leaders, calling them for talks.

The Serbs, however, knew from experience that talks with the Turks often ended in their death. They therefore did not obey Captain Kulin's summons, forcing him thus to go deeper and deeper into the rebellious country.

Yet the Turkish Captain realized after a while that further advances would be highly dangerous.

He remembered one of the Serbian leaders, Ivan Knezhevich, who used to come to him and bring the taxes the Serbs had to pay. Being a wise man, Ivan had succeeded in the past in maintaining quite good relations between the Turks and their Serbian subjects. Captain Kulin summoned Ivan now.

L

'Look, Ivan, you are the Serbian head of Semberiya, and I am the Turkish head of Bosnia. Let us, as equal in rank, be good friends henceforth, good friends, Ivan, and sworn brothers too!'

Ivan agreed, hoping that life would be somewhat easier for the Serbs on account of Kulin's professed friendly attitude. He left the Turkish camp and, returning to Semberiya, summoned all the village elders from the district and told them:

'Fear not Kulin henceforth, for *he* will not enslave you!'

After announcing the good news, Ivan went on, travelling through the district and collecting bread and other food for the Turkish army— as he was bound to do.

However, Captain Kulin did not stay idle either. Easter was hardly over when he rode his host to the village of Dobritch and called the Serbs:

'Come, Serbs, hold our horses for us! I shall never enslave honest men among you. As for the outlaws—that is a different matter, and we shall deal with them according to their merits!'

The villagers of Dobritch came, trusting him, but as soon as they reached the host, Kulin shouted an order: his Turks drew out their sabres and beheaded all the seventy-four honest trusting Serbs. They captured the head of the village, Iliya, and the priest, Phillip, and led them away, with their hands tied behind their backs.

The Turks ransacked the village, set fire to the Serbian homes, and took away three hundred Serbian girls and young women as their slaves, leaving only charred hearths and stones in the village.

When they returned to their camp they stuck the village-head, Iliya, and the priest, Phillip, on poles: they both died the most atrocious deaths. The enslaved womenfolk were taken to the tents and divided between the Turks.

Soon afterwards Ivan was on his way back with twelve of his men and the food for the Turkish host. As he approached the camp, he noticed that its look had changed: by every tent he saw women, Serbian women, who had not been there before.

Ivan knew what that meant, he knew that they were Turkish slaves and his heart ached with pity for them. He fainted with pain; when he recovered, tears were streaming down his kind face.

'What misfortune for the Serbs, my brothers! The Turks must have broken faith since they have done this to us!'

Yet he wiped his tears and even forced a smile on his face as he entered the Turkish camp. He greeted the Turks in their own language, adding:

'You have been lucky in your hunting, Turks. You have had a good catch, I see!'

'Yes, Ivan, a good catch, better than which we could never wish', they answered.

Ivan went by many Turkish tents and finally reached that of Kulin, all of shining silk. He entered it and greeted Kulin respectfully. Kulin answered in the same polite way, offering him a seat next to his own and handing him a cup of coffee.

'No, Kulin, my sworn brother, thank you; I shall neither sit nor drink coffee with you seeing that you have so deceived me. You have been hunting without me. Will you do me a favour and let me share the catch with you? I promise to give you, in return, a fair share of all I have caught on my own, Kulin.'

'Well spoken, Ivan my sworn brother! You will indeed have a share of my catch—I grant you the gift of thirty of my slave-girls now!'

Ivan bowed to Captain Kulin.

'Thank you, Captain Kulin, thank you for your gift, for the slave-girls you are granting me now!'

The Serbian women, hearing that thirty among them had been freed by Ivan, wept and wailed as one, rushing among the bewildered

Turks, stopping only when they reached Ivan. Each one of them tried to catch his sleeve, his arm or his hand, imploring:

'O Ivan, who are both father and mother to us now! Save us, for God's sake! Save us, do not let us stay in Turkish hands!'

Ivan wanted to leave the camp, but could not move, surrounded by all those desperate women. Although he wished to keep his pretence in the face of the Turks, tears overflowed from his eyes and he said to the enslaved women, trying to comfort them:

'Fear not your fate, my dear sisters; have heart and wait. I promise to ask the Serbs to help and free you all from your present plight.'

He retraced his steps and, coming to Kulin, spoke again:

'Dear sworn brother, Captain Kulin, will you do me a great favour? Sell all your slaves to me and name the price, however high you may deem it should be.'

'No, sworn brother Ivan, you will never be able to buy those slaves. I shall ask a ransom you can never give me and you will lose your own head on account of those poor slaves, Ivan.'

'Do not let that trouble you, sworn brother: you may ask a ransom of pure gold; do not pity either the slaves or me, Kulin.'

'You shall give me five loads of gold, Ivan!'

'I shall give you three loads, sworn brother, and you will give me all the slaves,' said Ivan, bowing low. He knew that all the Serbs put together could hardly scrape up so much gold, let alone five loads of it.

Kulin agreed, thinking that gold was far more useful than slaves in those unruly times.

'Will you take your slaves now, sworn brother? When will you bring the gold to me?' asked Kulin.

'I shall take the slaves with me now, sworn brother. As for the gold, I shall bring it later.'

'Have you good warrants for your word, Ivan?'

'I always have three warrants, Kulin: my first warrant is God Almighty, my second is an honest man's word, and my third warrant is my solemn promise not to deceive you, Kulin.'

'If you do not believe those, I shall bring you four others: four respectable, well-known Turks from Bosnia.'

The four Turks happened to be in the camp and they all confirmed Ivan's promise.

Ivan now hired several boats, and bade all the enslaved women to board them. They did so gladly, but the Turkish boatmen refused to row them across the river. Ivan rowed them all across himself, and with them in the last boat his own steed. Once on the other side, he mounted the horse and led the three hundred women to his own home in the town of Biyelina. He had plenty of bread baked for them and let them feast on all the best food and drink he had in his home.

Then he sent his men to go through all the land of Semberiya and to deliver his message to every village:

'Let the head of every family come to me; where there is no man in a home, let the widow come who rules the family instead of him; where there are childless women, let them come to Biyelina too.'

They all obeyed and arrived in Biyelina on the day Ivan had named. When he saw that the gathering was big, that there were as many people present as he could expect, Ivan walked among them, his face worn by great grief. He thus addressed the assembled Serbs:

'He who has no child of his own can open his heart now and embrace somebody else's offspring. He can buy a son or a daughter according to his wish and thereby save his soul too. . . .

'He who already has his own offspring can increase the number of his children by buying them a brother or a sister. He would be doing this for the love of God and for the rest of his own soul.

'If there are young men among you who have never had sisters, each one can have a dear sister now—he can buy her and ensure his soul's rest at the same time.

'Come, dear brothers, come and buy the slaves now, save the poor Serbians from the heathen Turkish hands, brothers!'

Hearing his words, all the Serbs of Semberiya came closer and began buying the slaves. Ivan accepted the money each of them offered; when the last slave was sold he saw that he had gathered hardly two loads of gold. Even by adding all that he had himself he could not make up the third. In the end he borrowed the rest from two honest Turks who trusted him.

As soon as he had enough gold, Ivan hastened back to Captain Kulin. How glad the Turk was at the sight of all that gold!

'Thank you, Ivan, thank you; there is nobody like you from here to Constantinople I warrant!'

Ivan lost no time in idle talk with him. He returned home and summoned all the Serbs who had answered his first call to come again. This time he waited by a church for them. As they arrived and gathered around him, Ivan said:

'Hear me, O Serbs, my dear brothers! Do not let the slaves you bought from me go hungry, or pine for their own people. Let them go wherever they wish to go, for there is no merit in buying slaves from the Turks and keeping them enslaved in our own homes. Let them go wherever they wish, brothers!'

All the Serbs agreed at once and let the slave-women go away.

Happy was Ivan, elated was his soul.

But—nobody remembered to say a word of thanks to Ivan, let alone to pay him back for what he had given!

Yet nobody, not Ivan himself, thought of it. God would remember it though, when Ivan's hour of death struck and when he presented himself in the face of God, the Righteous and Merciful.

THE BEGINNING OF THE SERBIAN
UPRISING AGAINST THE TURKS

 ALMIGHTY God, what strange things happened in Serbia when the Turkish rule was to be reversed, when others wanted to take over and deal justice to the people! The well-to-do Serbian village elders were not willing to quarrel with the Turks, nor were the greedy Turks disposed to quarrel with them. Those who wanted to fight were the poor Serbs—and most of them were poor —they were peasants who could pay no more taxes and would stand no more tyranny from the Turks. The priests were on their side, urging them to begin fighting, for the country was boiling, the earth seemed to be seething with blood coming out of the depths, and the time for fighting had come. One had to stand for the holy Cross once more after the battle of Kossovo, and once more shed one's own blood and avenge one's ancestors by it.

The Saints in Heaven started waging the war by disturbing the usual order of things in the clear sky over Serbia. The first unusual portent they caused in the sky was to bring out the moon, and let her appear every night from St. Tripun's up to St. George's Day, signalling

161

thus to the Serbs to take up their arms and begin fighting, but the Serbs did not dare to do so.

The second unusual portent was this: the Saints let blood-bespattered flags fly across the blue sky every day from St. George's to St. Demetrius's Day, signalling to the Serbs to take up their arms and begin fighting, but the Serbs did not dare to do so.

The third odd thing they did was to let thunders roll on St. Sava's Day, in midwinter, when thunders are unheard of. The dazzling lightning struck across the sky; the whole earth shivered; the trembling began in the east and spread to the west. The Saints were thus signalling to the Serbs again to take up arms and begin fighting, but the Serbs did not dare to do so.

The Saints decided to try once more. The fourth time they let the sun rise on a day in early spring, on St. Tripun's day. The sun rose above the horizon, and then sank beneath it again. Three times did the sun rise and sink, dancing in the pale eastern sky; three times did the day begin and three times did it end in the course of the same morning.

The Turks of Beograd were watching the strange happenings in the sky; all the seven high dignitaries who had rebelled against the Sultan and were ruling over Serbia on their own, stood at the windows in their own homes, unable to take their eyes off the horizon. They were: Aganliya and Kutchuk Aliya; the two brothers Fotchich; Mehmed-Aga and Mustaf-Aga; then Mula Yussuff, the highest ranked of them all; Dervish-Aga, the purveyor of bread for the army; and the oldest among them, the hundred-year-old Fotcho. They all repaired to the city gate where the road from Istanbul led to the town, all of them wrapped in fur-lined, scarlet cloaks. As they gathered, they looked at the sky again, greatly worried, all of them.

'What a strange sight, my friends,' said one of them. 'This portends no good for us.'

Greatly troubled and worried, the seven Turkish rebellious governors took a big glass dish, went down to the Danube and caught some of its water into the dish which they now carried up to the tower of Neboysha on the river bank. They put the dish on the top of the tower; the clear water reflected the stars still visible in the sky. The seven Turks sat around it to see their fortune in the water and to learn what was in store for them till the end of their lives. They all bowed above the water, and gasped, for not a single head was reflected in it! The infuriated Turks took their small battling-axes from under their belts, hit the glass dish angrily and broke it. They hurled the broken pieces down into the Danube so that no trace of the glass dish, and their bad fortune in it, should remain on firm soil.

That did not dispel their forebodings, though; they climbed down the tower together, and walked to a big inn. Sitting down, they put old Fotcho at the head of the table, his white beard falling down to his waist. A shout was heard from all of them:

'Make haste and come to us now, all you muezzins and wise men! Bring along your holy books and tell us what kind of future Fate has for us now!'

The muezzins and the wise men came, bringing their holy books. As they opened the yellow pages, all of them shed big, bitter tears.

'Turks, our brothers, O you seven noble lords, this is what our holy books tell us: it is five hundred years now that strange things like these we have seen lately appeared in the clear skies above Serbia; the Serbian Empire went down then and we came to rule over their lands. We beheaded two Christian Tsars then, Tsar Constantin in Constantinople, and Tsar Lazar on the Field of Kossovo. Milosh avenged Lazar by killing our Sultan Murat; Murat did not die on the spot and lived long enough to see that we had won the battle and were lords of Serbia. He called his Viziers to his tent and said to them:

' "Turks, my brothers, viziers and courtiers, I have won this country for you and I am dying now! Listen to me if you want your rule to be long and prosperous: do not be harsh with the vanquished people, be good and fair towards them instead. Let each head pay a tax of fifteen, even thirty dinars, but do not overtax them unduly, do not accuse them of crimes which they do not commit; do not touch their churches, their laws, and their honour; do not take revenge on them for Milosh's killing me, for that is a soldier's hard luck, the risk he has to take. *A kingdom cannot be won by sitting on soft cushions, smoking a pipe, and gazing peacefully.* Do not force the poor Serbs to leave their towns and villages and go to the woods for fear of you; be gentle with them as you would be with your own sons. Only if you heed my words, O Turks, will your rule be long and undisturbed. If, on the other hand, you should disobey me and be cruel to the vanquished people, you will lose what we won today, my friends."

'Our Sultan died and we remained alive, but neither our ancestors nor we ourselves did heed his warning: we were cruel and unjust with the

163

Serbs, we trod over their most sacred honour, we accused and punished them for all kinds of invented crimes, we forced them to pay many heavy taxes and, by doing all this, sinned heavily against Allah.

'Now that these strange things are happening in the sky, it is clear that someone will lose his rule. Do not fear any King, Turkish lords, for no King will attack a Sultan; no Kingdom would dare to threaten an Empire, for that is how God has arranged things in this world. Beware of the poor instead: when the poor peasants, armed with their pikes and spades, lift their heads and rebel against us, great trouble will come over us Turks; here, in Arabia and Syria, Turkish widows will be weeping for their lost sons and husbands.

'Moreover, Turks, our brothers, all you seven worthy lords, hear what our holy books say about you: all your houses will be devoured by flames, you will lose your heads, and on your hearths grass will soon grow. Our minarets will be covered by cobwebs, for there will be no muezzins to address their prayers to the Prophet from them! There where now our roads and cobbled streets are, there where proud Turks have been passing, their shod horses striking the stones, grass will grow and engulf it all: *the roads will long for the Turks, but there will no longer be Turks to tread them.* That is what our holy books say, O Turkish lords.'

All the seven Turks looked at the ground, dumbfounded, for no one can talk or argue with books. Old Fotcho gathered his beard into his hand and chewed it, thinking how odd all that was and how infuriating not to be able to persuade the books to alter what had been written so long ago and thus change their fate. The only one who kept his spirits alive was Mehmed-Aga Fotchich. He looked up, striking the table with his fist, and said:

'Out of my sight, muezzins and scholars! Go away and say your prayers to Allah, five times a day! Do not worry about us: as long as we are in good health and have sane minds, as long as we are in possession of the town of Beograd, we shall be able to govern the city as well as her surroundings and the miserable wretches living in them.

'If Kings will not attack us, why should we bother about those miserable peasants? Why, indeed, since there are seven of us, governors of the city, each of us having a store-room full of treasure! What kind of treasure? All of it soft glistening ducats! Moreover, four of us have each *two* such store-rooms, heaps of gold in coins innumerable. When we, the four of us, make up our minds, we will open our treasure vaults and strew the cobbled streets with our soft glistening gold; we shall raise a host with our ducats and shall divide it in four, like brothers, each of us commanding a fourth of it. We shall then visit all the seventeen districts which we govern now and shall slay all the Serbian heads of villages, all their chiefs, priests, and Serbian schoolmasters, all their menfolk, except the foolish seven-year-olds. Those boys will later be good servants to us Turks.'

Mehmed-Aga mentioned the names of those he particularly wanted to behead because they were respected by their own people and feared by the Turks.

'When I behead Black George, from the proud village of Topola,' he said after a while, 'him who trades with the Tsar in Vienna, him who is rich enough to buy all the ammunition the Serbs would need, I shall be content, for he will no longer be able to raise an army against us. Also, among other priests, I shall behead Hadji Djera and Hadji Ruvim, for they know the art of melting gold and writing with it. Yes, it is they who write letters to our Sultan and tell tales about us, their masters, whilst advising their flock how to disobey us and remain unpunished.

'There is another one I want to see dead: Iliya Birtchanin, for he has become impertinent, always riding that huge horse of his, with another one on the rein; he always carries a mace on his stirrup, and is terrifying to look at with his long thick moustaches folded under his helmet. So sure is he of himself that he lets no Turk step into his county; if he finds one, he breaks all his ribs with his mace and orders his men to carry the dying Turk away and "throw him somewhere where the ravens will not find his bones!" he says. And when he brings the taxes due to us, he comes armed into the council-hall; his right hand resting on his scimitar, he gives the money with his left. "Mehmed-Aga, here is your due. The poor send you their greetings and say that they cannot pay any more," he says. When I begin to count the money, he looks daggers at me: "Are you going to count the money, Mehmed-Aga? Why, I have already counted it!" he says. I throw the purse aside, eager to see him gone, for I dare not look at him.'

Mehmed-Aga mentioned some other Serbs who were in his way: proud, daring men who tried to preserve their and their people's dignity in the face of such self-willed, lawless rule as there was in Serbia during the days of the seven rebellious governors. 'And the priest, Melentiye, who had been to the Christian Holy Land across the seas, used that opportunity for visiting our Sultan and procuring, for a hundred ducats, a permit to build a church to the miscreant Serbs in the course of the next seven years. They built it within a year; it is six years now since it was finished and since he began building towers all round it, storing them secretly with ammunition and dragging big guns under cover of night into the towers: it is obvious that he expects something!

'When we behead those and all the other leading Serbs, what hope can the simple poor folk nurse then; how could they bother us, their armed, rich and mighty lords?'

As he uttered those last words all the other governors, except the oldest among them, leapt to their feet, bowed low to him and said:

'Thank you, our worthy friend, Mehmed-Aga! Your wisdom is equal to that of a Pasha! We shall indeed proclaim you Pasha and shall always obey you in all you say!'

The old man Fotcho stroked his white beard and said, looking through half-shut eyes at them all:

'What a youth, and what wisdom! What words brought him to a Pasha's soft seat!

'Take some straw into your white hand, my son, Mehmed-Aga, take it and wave it above roaring flames: will you thus put out the fire or will you blow it up greater? You may, since you have the means, raise such a host; you may, if you wish so, go into the country and ask one of the Serbian chiefs to come for talks with you; you may then break faith and behead him. You will lose your honour and behead one of them, but two others will escape. You will then behead two, but four others will escape. And it is those who will set fire to your homes; it is by their hands that you will be murdered.

'Therefore, do not act in that way, but heed my words, an old man's advice. I have been looking into our holy books myself, and I have learnt that this our rule is doomed; the rule is to go to other hands soon. It is much better for you to change your ways now and become kind, friendly, and gentle with the Serbs; lower the taxes, bearing in mind Sultan Murat's warning, and make friends with their priests. If you do all that, we may weather the stormy change of rule, for our rule will not last for long, brothers. Why should you wish for more gold? If you were to grind into flour the gold you already have, you would not be able to eat it all in your lifetime.'

Mehmed-Aga jumped up, flushing. 'No, old father, I will not obey you!'

166

The other five governors followed suit and went into action instantly. They dragged the big guns to the ramparts, raised an army of hired soldiers and divided it between the four great governors: Aganliya, Kutchuk Aliya, Mula Yussuff, and Mehmed-Aga. They soon departed into the country and summoned the Serbian elders for talks. The Serbs, believing their promise—by which they had warranted their safety—came, and were beheaded, each in his own village, some even in their own homes. Many brave honest Serbs and their priests perished then. Before long one of the most respected elders, Aleksa Nenadovich, came to the Turks and with him also Iliya Birtchanin. Mehmed-Aga tied their hands behind their backs himself and led them to the bridge over the river Kolubara. Seeing that he was to be beheaded, Aleksa turned to Mehmed-Aga:

'My lord, Fotchich Mehmed-Aga, grant me the gift of life now, and I shall give you six purses of golden ducats!'

'I would not let you go now even if you were to give me a hundred purses of gold, Aleksa,' said Mehmed-Aga, beaming with triumph.

'I shall give you a hundred purses of gold, my lord Fotchich Mehmed-Aga, if you grant me the gift of life now!' said Iliya Birtchanin.

'Do not be a fool, Iliya! Who would let a wolf from the mountains escape! Not I, for all the gold in the world!'

Mehmed-Aga shouted an order to the executioner who swung his sabre and cut off Iliya's head.

Aleksa sat down on the bridge, saying: 'May God strike dead any Christian who believes a Turk! Oh, Jacob, my own dear brother, do not believe the Turks, but kill them wherever you may come across them!'

Aleksa was about to say something else too, but the executioner forestalled him by cutting off his head.

When those two great Serbs fell, and another one, the priest Ruvim who was executed in Beograd on the very same day—in the same hour even—then the bright sun shining over their dead bodies grew dark all of a sudden.

Mehmed-Aga hastened to the guest-house where he was staying, hoping to catch and execute some more Serbs, but the news had spread around by then, and none of them answered Mehmed-Aga's summons to come to talks.

Mehmed-Aga realized that he had made a mistake by his rash judgement; he even repented his acts, but much too late. He called twelve of his most courageous and devoted soldiers and with them the man who always made coffee for him. Him he appointed their leader.

'Listen to me, my brave falcons! Mount the best horses now and ride as fast as you can to the village of Topola! Catch Black George and kill him, if possible, for if Black George should escape now, we are all doomed. Do as I bid you, good friends!'

The twelve horsemen galloped to the village of Topola on Saturday evening and arrived in the village at the crack of dawn on Sunday. They encircled George's homestead and shouted: 'Come out, George Petrovich!'

But who can deceive an angry dragon? Who can surprise him in his sleep?

George was wont to rise early in the morning, even before the crack of dawn, to wash, say his morning prayer, and drink a glass of plum brandy in his garden. That Sunday morning too George had already risen and, having washed and said his prayer, had gone to fetch some brandy from the cellar in one of his outhouses. He saw the Turks surrounding his home and did not answer their call. His young wife answered instead:

'God be with you, Turks! What are you looking for at this nightly hour! George was here in front of the house a little while ago and must have gone somewhere, only I do not know where.'

George saw and heard all of it. He counted the Turks, drank a glass of brandy, loaded his rifle, and took plenty of gunpowder and leaden bullets. Then he walked a little farther to the pen where his twelve swine-herds were sleeping. He woke them up and said:

'Dear brothers, my twelve swine-herds, arise and open the pen now; drive the swine out to go wherever they wish. As for you, load your rifles; if God wills that the victory should be ours today, I shall richly reward you later on, with gold and silver for your arms, and silk and velvet for your clothes, brothers.'

The swine-herds did his bidding eagerly: the swine were let out of the pen, the rifles loaded, and the twelve men followed George as he turned his back on the pen. They walked back and, when they were within sight of his home, George said to his men:

'Keep an eye on a Turk, each of you, my twelve swine-herds, but do not fire before you hear my rifle. I shall aim at the tall Mehmed, their leader.'

George stretched himself on the ground, keeping an eye on Mehmed, fired, and brought him dead off his big horse. The twelve rifles fired the next moment: six Turks were shot, and the other six rode wildly away.

George gathered in the village more men for his company, which now hurried in pursuit of the runaway Turks. The Serbs found them in a village inn some distance from Topola and beheaded them all, taking revenge for the slain Serbs.

George now dispatched letters to the Serbian heads of all the seventeen districts, to towns and villages alike, saying:

'Kill at once the Turkish man of authority in your place, take your womenfolk and children out of towns and villages for fear of revenge, and hide them in the woods.'

All the Serbs obeyed George: they took up their bright arms, killed the Turkish men of authority, and hid their own womenfolk and children in the woods.

Having thus started the Serbian uprising, George rode through all the districts of Serbia, burnt all the Turkish sentry posts, pulled down all the summer residences and inns which the Turks had built for their own pleasure, and attacked all the Turkish small towns, setting fire to them, executing the Turks and thus making the quarrel between Serbs and Turks very grave indeed.

The Turks still wished to believe that all this was not quite serious; yet it was, for the Serbs became heads in their own towns: the downtrodden people had risen as vigorously as grass pushing up from under the soil!

The Turks who escaped from the burnt small towns fled to bigger ones. George rode fast from one to the other of them, shouting:

'Listen, Turks inside this city! Open the city gates and give us those among you who have committed unjust, violent deeds against us Serbs, if you want to be left in peace, and to preserve the Sultan's towns unharmed. If you do not give us those vile men, remember this: these towns were built by our own people who laboured on them for nine long years, but that same people can pull them down in a single day! We can pull them down and if that should happen, nobody would be able to restore peace among us and the Sultan, not even all the seven Kings if they were to act as intermediaries! We shall fight then to the last man among us, to the last drop of blood in our veins!'

The terrified Turks wept and begged George to be merciful and to spare the Sultan's beautiful towns. They opened then the city gates, captured the vile, greedy men amongst them and handed them over to the Serbs.

When the Serbs took hold of them, they pulled off all their fine clothes—all the costly fur-lined jackets, gold-embroidered cloaks, all their fine white turbans, their shiny boots, and red slippers. They let the Turks run naked across the field, and, hitting them with their maces, asked every now and then: 'Well, my lord, what about our taxes now?'

George drew out his sabre in the middle of the field and chopped off all the evil heads. He then entered the towns and executed all the Turks who were guilty of crimes against the Serbs, letting the good ones go and christening those who were willing to embrace Christianity.

And that is how George came to rule over Serbia, making the sign of the holy Cross over her and protecting her by his own strong arm. Serbia's frontiers were the town of Vidin in the east, the river Drina in the west, the Field of Kossovo in the south, and Beograd in the north, on the confluence of two rivers, the place where the Sava flows into the Danube.

George spoke thus to the river Drina: 'O, Drina, you cool, green river, and noble border between Bosnia and Serbia! Soon the day will come for me to cross you and liberate the worthy country of Bosnia!'

But more than a century had to go by before Bosnia became free and able to resume a peaceful life.

THE BATTLE OF MISHAR

wo black ravens flew from the white town of Shabats and the battlefield of Mishar, their beaks all red with blood, their legs blood-bespattered too. They flew over the rich plain along the river Sava; then flew over Drina's unruly emerald waters; they flew over the honourable country of Bosnia until they came to the west, where they stopped in the town of Vakuf, to rest on the Turkish Captain Kulin's white tower. As soon as they folded their weary wings they both croaked hoarsely.

Captain Kulin's wife heard them and climbed up the tower, saying:

'Oh my brothers, you two black ravens, do you come from the field of Mishar, by the white town of Shabats? Have you seen the numerous Turkish hosts around the town; have you seen the Turkish commanders and among them my beloved master, my lord Captain Kulin, who is at the head of a hundred thousand soldiers?

'Have you seen him who had pledged to our Sultan that he would restore peace to Serbia, that he would collect the taxes the Serbs owe us, and, moreover, catch Black George and send him alive to the Sultan? He also vowed that he would slay all the Serbian leaders who had started this quarrel with the Turks.

'Has he sent George to the Sultan?

'Has he put Jacob alive on a pole to die in deadly pain?

'Has he slayed Luka alive? Has he cut off Tchupich's head with his own sabre? Has he restored peace to Serbia?

'Is my lord Captain Kulin returning to me, leading with him the host

M   171

from proud Bosnia? Is he going? Shall I soon set eyes on him, tell me?

'Do his men drive the fat cows from the plains along the Sava; do they bring us Serbian slave girls who will be my devoted servants? When will my Kulin be here, tell me, ravens, so that I may prepare a worthy welcome for him?'

'O our lady, Captain Kulin's young wife, we would like to be bearers of good news to you, but here is the truth. We are coming from the white town of Shabats, and we have been over the vast field of Mishar: we have seen innumerable Turkish hosts and their commanders.

'We have seen your lord, Captain Kulin, and we have also seen the Serb Black George. George had but fifteen thousand Serbs, whereas your Kulin had a hundred thousand Turks. We were there and saw with our own eyes when the two hosts clashed in the vast field of Mishar—the Serbian and the Turkish host, fair lady. The Serbs carried the day, fair lady. Your Kulin fell on the battlefield slain by George Petrovich's own hand. Thirty thousand Turks fell with him, all the Turkish commanders, one better than the other, fair lady, all of them from proud Bosnia.

'Captain Kulin is not coming to you, he is not coming, and you will never see him again! Do not expect him, nor look out for him. Bring up your son as a warrior and send him to the Sultan's host to continue the battle, for Serbia is not to be appeased, fair lady!'

AUTHOR'S NOTE

THE Serbian folk ballads sprang up not long after the tragic defeat of the Serbs at the Field of Kossovo. Until this battle the Serbian empire had been wealthy and prosperous, while not so long before it had been a very powerful State. When, therefore, the ballads first were sung, the memory of the Turkish conquest was still poignant and painful to the Serbian people. At the same time, the battle was distant enough for the descendants of those who fell in it to grasp the full meaning of their defeat, and to mourn their loss of freedom, for bitter experience had already taught them what that meant. *Raya*, as the Sultan's Christian subjects were called, were exposed to the cruelty and impetuous whims of the Turkish feudal lords. Men were tortured and beheaded for little or no reason; women and children were abducted by force—boys made to serve in the Turkish army and girls taken to harems or to slave markets in the vast Ottoman Empire. Civilised life, which during the Nemanyichi dynasty (from the twelfth to the second half of the fourteenth century) had been highly developed, suddenly gave way to utter darkness and misery.

Those were the times in which anonymous poets created the ballads and sang of the past glory and greatness of valiant heroes, Kings and Tsars. Their persons, their castles (or 'white mansions'), their arms, and their clothes were endowed with a beauty and splendour that only nostalgic imagination could lend them. Those memories were the only solace of the Serbian people, who drank in the words of the poems as a thirsty man drinks water in a desert. And because of the ballads, the battle for the 'Holy Cross and the Golden Freedom' was never irretrievably lost in the minds of the people, who were unwilling to accept meekly their tragic defeat. Not without reason did a Serbian poet, Jovan Jovanović-Zmaj, say once: 'The poem has kept us alive, and we are thankful to it', for, to the Serbs, these words were true indeed. The ballads, orally transmitted from one generation to another, most often sung by bards to the accompaniment of the national instrument, the *gusle* (a primitive string instrument), kept the spirit of freedom alive throughout five centuries, in spite of overwhelming despondency and gloom.

As clashes between the Turks and the Serbian outlaws (most of whom lived in the woods) continued even after the Serbian State had ceased to exist, new ballads were sung about the exploits of knights and outlaws. These ballads date from the sixteenth century onwards, and belong to a later period than the first three parts of this book. Then, during the first uprising against the Turks (1804–13), a blind bard, a *guslar* by the name of Filip Višnjic, also sang of these outlaws, and thus he too played a part in the general struggle for better days. All these ballads, both the earlier and the later ones, were the inspiration behind many an attempt to recover freedom, until victory was finally won.

The tragic element in the cycles, describing the decline and defeat of the once-great Serbian State, have a depth and poignancy equal to the greatest tragedies in world history. The mother of the Yugovichi, for instance, personifies all mothers who have searched the battlefield for the bodies of their fallen sons, throughout the ages, from the time when wars were first waged to the present day. But beside the tragedy, the ballads abound with hard, ringing truths which stand out as though carved in granite, and which, with time, have become so much a part of the national character that they are interwoven into everyday speech, just as Shakespeare's lines have become part of the English language.

Those who strove to survive, and fought for a life of justice and dignity, had indeed to be optimistic, and the ballads show an irrepressible sense of humour which relieves the tragedy: Milosh Voyinovich, for example, figuring as an uncouth Bulgarian shepherd at his uncle's wedding; Kralyevich Marko's behaviour in many of the ballads, and so on.

Some of the Serbian ballads, first handed down by oral tradition, were put into writing from the sixteenth century on, but it was only in the nineteenth century that they received due attention. Circumstances were then more favourable, and thanks to a most gifted Serb, the self-taught scholar of high repute, Vuk Karadžić, the ballads were at last made known in Europe. Karadžić was deeply interested in folk-lore, and collected ballads, tales, proverbs, and sayings, which were published in Vienna. They aroused great admiration and interest among the Romantic poets: Goethe translated one of the ballads into German; Prosper Mérimée translated others into French; the brothers Grimm also translated some of them. Soon the Serbian ballads were known in many European countries.

This book is an attempt to bring them closer to English-speaking readers.

A few words of explanation concerning the transcription of proper names are perhaps necessary here. As the correct spelling of Serbian names often seems to an English reader unpronounceable (for example, Mrnjavčević), I have tried to give a phonetic rendering of such proper names, which should make them more recognizable to an English person—who may perhaps wish to read them aloud. The vowels in Serbian names should be read as follows:

a as in Marko
e „ red
i „ ship
o „ log
u „ put

I also feel that the following explanation of a few names and some Serbian customs might help the reader towards a better understanding of the ballads.

GLOSSARY

CADI
A Turkish judge. The judges were notorious for their readiness to accept bribes, hence the Serbian proverb: 'It's the *Cadi* who accuses you, the *Cadi* who judges you.' Very few Serbs had a fair hearing at the Turkish law-courts.

EFFENDI
Turkish form of address, equivalent to 'Sir'.

KOLO
A dance, usually performed in the village square on feast-days. Most villages have their own variety of *kolo*, which is usually danced to a lively rhythm, but there are slow-moving, dignified versions as well. The dancers hold hands, moving in a reel and singing, accompanied by string instruments, shepherd's pipes, trumpets, or wind-pipes like those in Scotland, and, in the South, by drums.

KUM, KOOM
A witness at a wedding (and also a godfather). The relationship between the *koom* and the married couple (the bridegroom is also called a *koom*, and the bride a *kooma*) is sacred in Serbia, and considered equal to that between parent and child. That is why a marriage between a *koom* and *kooma* (the daughter of the *koom*) was unthinkable. Very often in the past, two families have kept up this relationship for generations.

LATINS
In and around Montenegro, 'Latins' are Roman Catholics (probably because their service is in Latin). Serbs and Montenegrins are Greek-, or rather Serb-Orthodox, and their service is in the old Slavonic language. In the Serbian folk ballads, Latins are always a 'shrewd, cunning race', perhaps because of their diplomacy—which enabled a small State like Venice to subdue almost the whole of the Adriatic.

177

MUEZZIN	The Moslem priest who calls his prayer to Allah from the minaret.
PATRON SAINT'S DAY or SLAVA	Each family in Serbia has a patron saint, and honours him by celebrating his day lavishly. A special breadcake is taken to the Church to be blessed, with a dish of specially prepared wheat which is served to all the guests. A big wax candle, also blessed in Church, burns under the icon of the saint. The head of the house stands all day long in honour of the saint to receive his guests. The house is open to everyone on that day, and all the friends and acquaintances of the family are meant to remember it and come, uninvited.
STARI SVAT	Also a witness at a wedding. His relationship to the bridegroom is also sacred, and he has special duties at the wedding ceremony.
VILA	A fairy. Unlike other fairies, she is supposed to be of normal height, and of course of exceptional beauty. Besides mountain fairies, there are also sea and land fairies. They are like human beings: they can be helpful and good-natured, but also jealous and revengeful.
WEDDING-TRAIN	Weddings are very ceremonial affairs in the ballads, especially if the Tsar or any of the great lords are involved. The bridegroom would collect his relatives, friends, and servants, all arrayed in their most festive clothes, and together they would ride with flags and musicians to take the bride from her parents.
YANITCHARI	A special body of the Turkish army, feared for its ruthlessness and cruelty.
YATAGHAN	A Turkish curved sabre, similar to a scimitar.

178

PRINTED IN GREAT BRITAIN
AT THE UNIVERSITY PRESS, OXFORD
BY VIVIAN RIDLER
PRINTER TO THE UNIVERSITY